Rosamond Richardson started her career designing fabrics for Liberty's. She then presented two series for BBC television in the UK which, with their accompanying publications, led her into writing. She is the author of several books based on interviews including *Talking about Bereavement* and *The Long Shadow: inside Stalin's Family*. Rosamond has written many best-selling vegetarian cookery books.

books by the same author include

Talking about Bereavement
The Long Shadow: inside Stalin's Family

Eileen's Story

ONE WOMAN'S INSPIRATIONAL TRIUMPH OVER TERMINAL CANCER

Rosamond Richardson

ELEMENT
Rockport, Massachusetts • Shaftesbury, Dorset
Melbourne, Victoria

© Element Books Limited 1997
Text © Rosamond Richardson 1997

First published in the USA in 1997 by
Element Books, Inc.
PO Box 830, Rockport, MA 01966

Published in Great Britain in 1997 by
Element Books Limited
Shaftesbury, Dorset SP7 8BP

Published in Australia in 1997 by Element Books
and distributed by Penguin Australia Limited,
487 Maroondah Highway, Ringwood, Victoria 3134

Page design by Roger Lightfoot
Typeset by WestKey Limited, Falmouth
Printed and bound in the USA by Courier Westford, Inc.

Library of Congress Cataloging in Publication data available

British Library Cataloguing in Publication data available

ISBN 1–86204–057–5

Contents

Introduction

When Eileen was diagnosed with lymphoma at the age of forty-six she was told that her condition was at the no-hope stage and that she had only a matter of months to live. Bluntly, she was told that she had terminal cancer. A bank manager's wife, mother of three young children, Eileen was living a middle-class life typical of millions of women in the Western world.

The difference with Eileen is that she refused to accept the death sentence. Through an extraordinary experience, a 'miracle' as she describes it, she discovered a life-force within herself. Taking her destiny in her own hands, she embarked on a journey which has led her, through many ups and downs, back to health and complete recovery.

This is an extraordinary story, told by an ordinary person-in-the-street, which will give hope and inspiration to everyone who reads it. Most of us know someone who has or has had cancer. Eileen tells her compulsive saga with a passionate belief in the power of the mind over sickness and health, in the supreme importance of looking after the body, and in the close connection between the two.

Although the treatment which Eileen chose was an expensive one, one that initially she could not afford, it was made possible by extraordinary 'coincidences' which seemed like miracles to her, and the generosity of friends, no less miraculous. But it was by no means the cost alone that bought the cure: a parallel story in the book about a very rich woman called Yvonne, makes the point that wealth cannot buy you your life. In her case, in spite of spending money on various treatments, her fear conquered her will to live. Eileen's did not. This is the core of her story: the will and the courage to live, along with the cleansing of the body and coming to terms with the past, are key factors in the struggle for survival.

Eileen is now living a normal life again with her husband and children, flagrantly flaunting her prognosis of imminent death. She now counsels cancer patients who are going through the gruelling processes that she endured. Her experiences have changed her life as well as giving it back to her, and they have changed the lives of those close to her. Her story will change the life of everyone who reads it.

This is Eileen's story.

PART 1

Death Sentence

If you want to get at the kernel you must break the shell.

MEISTER ECKHART

1

I had never really been in control of my life. I used to think that the things that happened to me were totally outside my control, they were just 'fate'. For as long as I can remember, my view of things was that whatever happened to me, there was nothing I could do about it. I also had a very pessimistic view of life, thinking that things would always go wrong rather than right.

Around Easter 1990 I tried to get out of bed one morning and couldn't. My back had completely seized up. I'd never had a back problem before. Edward helped me to get out of bed and said, 'I'll take you to the doctor, something is obviously wrong.'

My GP suggested I go to an osteopath. The osteopath did some manipulation, and she happened to notice that I'd got a swelling in my groin. She said it was highly likely that it was a hernia. I should go back to my GP and get him to look at it.

'No, it isn't a hernia,' he said. 'It's a slightly enlarged lymph node. It's nothing to worry about. I'm sure that if you go on holiday and relax, it'll go away.'

So off I went on a camping holiday to France with the children. The swelling remained, but it didn't bother me – I just noticed it when I showered. Everything was fine until the day we were coming home, when I felt very ill. We had a long hot drive to the Channel port and my chest began to feel tighter and tighter. I had to lie down and by the time we got home I was feeling terrible. Next morning I couldn't speak, and my throat had closed up.

I went to my GP the next day. 'You've got a very nasty chest infection,' he said.

'While I'm here,' I replied, 'I should mention that I've still got this lump in my groin.'

'Well, I'm going to give you some antibiotics for the chest infection, and whatever the lump is, it will go away.'

I embarked on the course of antibiotics. The chest infection went, but the lump didn't. It didn't hurt, but it was quite pronounced. I was just thinking that I would have to go back to the doctor again when I started to get bleeding and spotting, which I had never had before. I went back to see him *again*: I hardly ever had to see him usually!

He gave me an examination and said there was some bleeding but it all looked very healthy. However, the lump was slightly enlarged, and as it had been there for at least a couple of months we ought to do something about it.

'What do you think it is?'

'Oh, I don't think it's anything serious! You've most probably got an infection somewhere which needs something stronger than antibiotics. We'll need to investigate it.'

'How do we do that?'

'Well, the best thing is for you to go and have a biopsy so that we can see what it is.'

So it was arranged that I should go into a private clinic, which meant I wouldn't have to wait. He knew the surgeon, who was an expert at doing this operation. 'There is a main artery that runs down there, so it's important that you get someone who knows what he is doing. I'll get in touch with him and he will contact you.'

The surgeon, Mr Eley, contacted me within a few days and I went to see him. When he examined my lump he said, 'Goodness me, it's so small it's hardly worth bothering about. But as your GP is a friend of mine, come in next week and we'll have a look at it.'

Everybody was very nonchalant about it, so I really was not that concerned. Their attitude was so casual that I was hardly worried.

2

Edward and I had met in the summer of 1975 and were married in February 1976. I'd had quite a few long relationships before then, but had always managed to destroy them in some way. I needed the *soul* of a man before I could believe that he could genuinely love me. I had this fear that all that men wanted was sex, so they had to tread hot coals for me before I could believe in them, or give myself physically. The year before I met Edward, my sister had died of cancer and I was very depressed. I felt very unhappy, tired and unwell.

Just before we got married, the bank Edward works for told him they were moving him out of London, to the area where we still live now. We were both thirty-one and decided that we wanted children straight away. Our first son was born in September 1977, the second in September 1979. We decided that we weren't going to have any more children because I was thirty-five. Then a lovely mistake occurred! Helen was born in April 1982.

Edward works as a sales manager for the bank, so he moves about from branch to branch and travels quite a lot. He originally wanted to be a farmer, and he did farm for a little while, but his father, who was a bank manager, continually reminded him about the need for security. So in a way he has spent most of his life doing a job that really he didn't want to do. He says to me now, 'If I won the lottery tomorrow, I would give up this job and go and buy a remote place in the country where I could grow organic vegetables.' Edward has this hankering for the land; he loves gardening and likes walking – he goes off with the dog for hours at a time.

During the first years of our marriage, I was happy and yet I wasn't happy. Nothing had changed; I still had this tiredness. One man I went out with for quite some time, who was always full of energy, used to say to me, 'Oh come on, you're always asleep, you're always tired.'

And I was. Because, although I didn't know it at the time, I was weighed down by huge amounts of emotional problems that I had been repressing all my life. It was draining me, sucking out my energy and blocking it. I had a lot of sexual hang-ups and I didn't know where they were coming from.

On the surface everything appeared fine, but underneath it wasn't really. Part of me thought that once I had my 'perfect family' everything was going to be all right. I was always striving for more; but every time I got it, things were no better. It was a constant, insatiable hunger. I always had to be shopping, buying things, spending money. It was as though if I had a new *thing*, everything would be all right. But of course, it wasn't. Nothing was going to change.

For me, this was an addiction pattern, constantly seeking comfort in things, looking for things, having beautiful things around me. But it didn't make things right because I was just feeding the addiction.

We were not unhappy, but I don't think that we were really *happy*. We weren't connecting on all levels, but neither of us knew why. I was always very worried about other people's opinions and that used to drive Edward mad. I would worry terribly about what other people thought. Edward, on the other hand, is a fairly extrovert person and he doesn't care a damn: he is motivated by his own desires, not by a wish to be thought well of by others. He was more secure in himself; I was less so. Concern about what other people were thinking was part of my addiction pattern, and it used to irritate him that I was so unsure and uncertain.

3

I went into the clinic one lunchtime towards the end of September 1990. Mr Eley came to see me.

'We're going to put you out, I'll do a very small cut, take out a little bit of the lymph node and stitch you up again. Just a tiny little incision and you can go home tomorrow.'

I was given the pre-med and taken down to theatre. I don't remember anything else until I woke up: it was obviously the middle of the night. I had been operated on at three o'clock in the afternoon, but it was much, much later. I wanted to go to the toilet and I got out of bed feeling very woozy. Then I saw the *enormous* dressing on my abdomen. 'Gosh, that's a big dressing,' I thought, and when I lifted the pad, I saw that the incision had been huge, not the tiny one I had expected. I was quite shocked. But I was still woozy and went back to sleep.

The next morning was the first indication I had that something was wrong. When the nurse came in, I asked her about the size of the wound.

'Mr Eley will be coming to see you shortly.'

When he came into the room, he wouldn't look at me. Immediately I felt a cold hand clutching at my heart. He had been so smiling and nonchalant about it all. Suddenly that had all changed. He was looking everywhere but at me; until then we'd had eye contact and he had been charming and pleasant. Now suddenly his attitude was different.

'Why have I got such a large incision?' I asked.

'Well, the node was much deeper than I thought,' he said, still avoiding my eyes.

'What do you think it was?'

'Oh, I don't know, I can't possibly say. It will have to go to the lab and be analysed.'

'You must have some idea because you've obviously seen lots of nodes.'

'No, I couldn't possibly say. It will have to go to the lab.'

I was feeling quite panic-stricken by now, not because of anything he said, but at what he *didn't* say. From the way he was behaving, I knew that something was wrong, that it was something bad. But for some reason, the thought of cancer did not enter my head.

I was told I could go home later on that day, and that I would have to go back in a week to have the stitches removed. I went home and was very, very anxious. Mr Eley promised me that he would call me as soon as he had the results. I was hoping that by the middle of the next week I would hear something, but by the following Thursday, he still hadn't called. Half of me was saying that it couldn't be anything sinister otherwise he would have telephoned me, the other half was saying that there must be something wrong.

In some ways, you marry the person you need – the eternal pessimist, me, with the eternal optimist, Edward. He kept saying, 'Oh, I'm sure it's going to be all right. Don't worry.' At times he infuriated me by his optimism, but it was the balance I needed.

I was so on edge, and being so awful, that he said to me, 'You must call him before the weekend. You can't go through another weekend feeling like this.'

'Yes, I will. I'm definitely going to call him if he hasn't called me by Friday morning.'

Friday came and I hadn't heard from him, so I said to Edward, 'I'm going to call him this morning. I'll go and shower, then I'll phone him.'

I had just got out of the shower when the telephone rang. It was the GP's receptionist.

'I'm just telephoning to see if you could come and see the doctor. He'd like to see you.'

'Oh, has he got the results of my biopsy?'

'Oh . . . yes, I think that's what it's about. But,' she said, 'it's not urgent, so you don't have to come today!'

In view of what was to come, that was incredible.

'I want to come today, I need to speak to him before the weekend.' I arranged an appointment for an hour's time.

I have thought about this many times. It was appalling that, knowing what they were going to tell me, they didn't tell me to bring someone with me.

I put the phone down and was getting dressed when a strange thing happened. A friend in the village, who knew I was worried, phoned me and said, 'Have you got the results of your biopsy yet?'

'They've just phoned and I'm going to see the doctor now.'

'Do you want me to take you?'

'Oh no, it's all right.'

'No, no, I'll take you' she insisted.

So, as it happened, she drove me there.

4

I shall never forget arriving at the surgery. I sat down and my GP said to me, 'I don't want you to panic at what I'm going to tell you.'

Immediately I went into total panic. 'What is it?'

He was very careful not to mention the word cancer. 'You've got something called lymphoma.'

I hadn't a clue what it was. I had never heard of it.

'What's that?'

Even though he was very vague about it all, I went into a state of total shock. The fact that he was evading telling me what was wrong gave me a double dose of fear. It seemed to confirm a deep premonition that something terrible was going to happen to me.

'I want you to come back on Monday with your husband and we can discuss what sort of treatment you should have.'

My friend Pam, who was waiting for me outside, later said that my face was like death when I came out.

'What's the matter?' she said.

I couldn't speak. It was as if someone had said, 'You are going to die tomorrow. This is *it*.'

Never in your wildest dreams do you think it is going to happen to you. Because cancer is a disease that comes from within us and grows, it doesn't make its presence felt. It creeps stealthily up on you and then suddenly rears its head. It's because you haven't been in tune with yourself that it's been allowed to grow, and when suddenly it makes its presence felt, it is saying 'it's too late'. When people with cancer phone me up now, so frightened and full of fear, I remember what it was like. It is the most unbelievable experience; it's impossible to describe. You have to experience it to know what it's like. I felt completely powerless, totally helpless. Nobody could help me. I was alone.

Pam and I got into the car and sat there with our arms around each other, sobbing. She didn't really know why I was crying. At first I couldn't bring myself to tell her what he had told me. Eventually, when I told her, she tried to be positive and say the right things, as people do. It was awful. I have delivered the same platitudes to other people before ('Oh well, you mustn't give up hope'), when inside I didn't really believe it. Suddenly I was hearing people saying that to me and I was thinking, 'They don't mean it, they're just saying it to make me feel better.'

I got home and from then on it was just like being in a pit. I was going to die. I telephoned Edward who said, 'I'll come home.'

I replied, 'There's nothing anyone can do. I'm going to die.'

There was no comfort anywhere. Nowhere. Whatever anyone said to me, I distrusted it. Even down to the doctors whom I suspected weren't telling me the truth. All my feelings were negative, and I was full of fear and distrust.

It was all very dramatic. My children came home from school and they knew something was very wrong, but since I couldn't properly acknowledge it myself, I certainly couldn't talk to anyone else about it. It was just too awful to contemplate.

The next day I had to go back to the clinic to have the stitches removed, feeling angry with Mr Eley who hadn't bothered to contact me at all. As soon as he knew it was something bad, he had passed the buck to my GP. He wasn't even there that day. The nurse removed the stitches which was very painful because it was a huge incision, right in the groin. It was a bit nasty-looking. She knew what the diagnosis was and I was tearful and upset.

I will always remember coming out and saying to Edward, 'I want to go into the shopping centre on the way home.'

I went into the bookshop to find every book I could about cancer. They were all full of doom and gloom, but I couldn't stop myself. Edward kept telling me not to look at them, but it was a compulsion. I had to.

5

We went back on Monday to see our GP. His use of words was amazing.

'We can give it a squirt of something.'

A squirt of something. Not 'chemotherapy'. A squirt.

He told me the options of where I could have this 'squirt': at the local hospital, where Mr Eley practised, or at a specialist centre. My GP favoured the latter: 'If you were my wife, I would rather you go to a specialist centre because lymphoma, as far as cancers go, is relatively rare and the hospital only sees two or three cases a year, whereas the Centre is dealing with them all the time.'

So we decided to go to St Lucy's in London. St Lucy is the patron saint of the blind.

My GP found out that there was a sympathetic woman consultant there. He got in touch with her straight away and asked her to take me. We got an appointment the following week.

Edward and I went together. The consultant was kind, but very frank. Up to this point, no one had said very much. She was the opposite and was almost brutally frank. At the time it was a terrible shock, but with hindsight, it was probably a very good thing. She told me I had lymphoma, as did all the fifty patients sitting outside. This amazed me because then it was relatively unusual, and it seemed a lot. Today, lymphoma has reached epidemic proportions. It is the fastest spreading cancer worldwide. In just four years it has gone almost out of control.

They wanted their own lab to look at the biopsy, and they wanted me to have a body scan and a bone-marrow biopsy. The scan was really scary. I had never been in one of those machines before. You lie there with people on the other side of a screen watching you. A dye goes into your veins and you have to lie there as a cover comes over you. The whole thing is frightening and claustrophobic.

But the bone-marrow biopsy was the worst. They had told me it was going to be painful, but it really was *excruciating*. I had to lie on my side with a nurse sitting behind me facing my back, and Edward in front of me holding my hand. I couldn't see what was going on behind me. Edward was fine until he saw the nurse pick up this huge instrument, like a giant corkscrew. They had anaesthetized the skin, but they had told me they couldn't anaesthetize the bone so I knew it was going to hurt. Edward could see her brandishing this tool and I could see him going greener and greener. Suddenly she said to him, 'I think you should go outside.' She thought he was going to pass out. I could feel some pressure, but couldn't see what was happening.

Another nurse came in to hold my hand and then this thing hit my bone. The pain was like nothing I've ever experienced or ever want to again. I screamed at full volume. It was over in a flash, but the pain was terrible.

You have this diagnosis and then all these awful things begin to happen to you. You wonder how you can escape, and if there will ever be an end to it. I was in this pit, this hell, this torment. I had no control over what was happening; I had been handed over, having all these awful things done to my body that were destroying my soul. Just the act of going through those things is enough to kill you off.

They told me to come back in a few days for the results of the scan. We went back and saw the woman consultant who had the scan in front of her.

'I've got some good news and some bad news.'

I was sitting there with my hands clenched, thinking, 'Please, please give me some hope. Say it's not going to be bad.'

'The good news is that you have a low-grade lymphoma, which means that it is slow-growing. But the bad news is that it is incurable. It's treatable, but it is not curable.'

Part of me wanted to know more, part of me didn't. I looked at Edward. He was so stunned that all the colour had gone from his face. This was the first time I had seen him in complete shock.

'What do you mean?'

'Well, we can treat it with chemotherapy, but it will keep coming back. As it comes back, it becomes less treatable.'

In other words . . .

'The other bad thing is that the scan shows that the disease is very extensive, particularly in your pelvic area.'

I found out afterwards that they grade cancers stage one, two three and four. Mine was stage four, the no-hope grade.

'I'm afraid the bone-marrow biopsy shows that it is also in the bone marrow.'

You can imagine what it felt like. When we had gone in, there was still some hope. Then suddenly that was taken away too. She had told me that I was going to die.

6

I can't remember much about what happened next. We were both in a complete daze. We didn't know what to say, it was numbing.

Then she said, 'We're going to start you on chemotherapy straight away.'

She went on to tell me that they were experimenting with bone-marrow transplants. This was an extremely risky business, so it was a last resort. I was young enough to be included in that trial because I was only forty-six.

She also told me that they were doing a trial with interferon, a virus-inhibiting substance which the body manufactures itself. She explained that they were re-evaluating its synthetic use and asked if I would consider participating in the trial. At that stage I was prepared to try anything. So it was decided that I was going to have the chemotherapy with interferon.

I was shown how to take the chemotherapy tablets every day at home, and how to inject myself three times a week with the interferon. She told me that it would give me flu-like symptoms and that I would feel ill, but that although the chemotherapy drug might cause a little nausea, I wouldn't have any great problems with it. I wasn't going to lose my hair.

She explained that the disease was fairly advanced and that the scan showed lesions on my liver and spleen. On the train journey home we both sat there without saying a word, gripping each other's hands. I felt totally pessimistic about the future: it was just a question of time.

The scan report read:

24.10.90. CT CHEST, ABDOMEN AND PELVIS: there is axillary nodal enlargement, without obvious mediastinal abnormality. No focal lung lesion is seen. Scans through the liver taken before and after IV contrast enhancement show two focal low attenuation lesions. One

is tiny and too small to characterize. The other is slightly larger which could represent a small deposit or might possibly relate to partial voluming from fat related to the ligamentum teris. The spleen is not enlarged. Both kidneys appear normal. There is extensive para-aortic, bilateral pelvis and bilateral inguinal node enlargement.
CONCLUSION: Axillary, para-aortic, pelvic and inguinal lymph node enlargement. Equivocal focal low attenuation lesions within the liver.

I realized just how much it had affected Edward: he was normally able to talk, but now he couldn't. Until then he had believed it would be all right, and suddenly the consultant had said that it wouldn't. From his point of view, he was going to be left alone with three young children. So my husband, who had always been both rock solid and laid back, was absolutely dumbstruck. The colour had drained from his face and he didn't know what to say. He wanted to help me, but he couldn't.

I withdrew into myself and all I could see was that I was going to die. Everything else was overshadowed by that. Nobody could help me in those first few days. Edward became very stressed and depressed because he could see me sinking further and further into this hole, and he was powerless to help. The children too became morose because they knew something terrible was going on, but I couldn't tell them what it was. I hadn't come to terms with it myself so I couldn't talk about it to anybody else. I was like a zombie. My only thought was, 'I'm going to die and this is it.'

Two weeks later the following letter from the consultant arrived for my GP:

... The biopsy shows a centro-blastic/centrocytic follicular lymphoma. The bone-marrow aspirate and trephine biopsies are in keeping with this diagnosis. CT scans show extensive intra-abdominal and pelvic disease. The patient is symptomatic in that she complains of left-sided back pain which is probably due to para-aortic lymphadenopathy and it would therefore seem reasonable to treat her now rather than waiting any longer.

We are currently evaluating the use of chlorambucil and interferon in a randomized comparison against conventional therapy, i.e. chlorambucil alone. She has agreed to take part in the study and has in fact been randomized to receive the combination. She is taking chlorambucil 10mg units thrice weekly subcutaneously. She has been taught to give the injections to herself. Generally speaking, this treatment is well-tolerated, although I have warned her that initially she

may have flu-like symptoms following interferon injections. We will
see her again in two weeks time.

That first week must have been so frightening for the children. I
wanted to lock myself away until I died, so I shut myself in my
room and cried and cried. I couldn't do anything. They must have
wondered what was happening, what was going on. I couldn't
tell them. They knew that I was sick, and they kept saying to me,
'What have you got? What is it?' and I kept saying, 'It's nothing
to worry about'. Helen, the eight-year-old, would say, 'Are you
going to die, Mummy?' and I would say, 'No, of course I'm not
going to die!'.

I couldn't *bear* to tell them that I had cancer at the beginning.
They were so full of fear, because they knew something awful was
happening. They were so frightened. The hardest thing for me
was the fact that my children were all quite young. The boys were
twelve and ten, and Helen was eight. The worst thing of all was
that I wasn't going to see them grow up. Every time I saw them,
I felt terrible grief at the thought of not being there. Those feelings
were *unbearable*. The fact that you are going to lose your partner
is painful, but you can't compare it with the feelings for your
children. We all know that one day we might lose our partner, but
we can't bear to think that we might lose our children. It's the most
terrible experience. How would they cope without me? How
could they exist without me to look after them? What would
happen to them?

I was terrified. It's the most horrible feeling that you can have.
The feeling of powerlessness is difficult to describe. It was there
twenty-four hours a day, and it was worse at night. I used to wake
up in the dark when the house was quiet and everyone was asleep
and then I felt really alone. It was just me and my thoughts. I
would often wake Edward with my crying.

I can remember saying to him, 'If you remarry, please have
someone who is going to be kind to the children.'

'As if I would! How could you possibly think that?'

But I couldn't bear to think of them with a step-mother who
wasn't kind to them. We had such a close loving relationship.

7

You need love more than anything at this time, but I couldn't accept love from anyone. I was on my own. I couldn't think about anything else. My thoughts were full of terror and despair. Death sat on me; I was squashed by it and there was no escape. It was like being in prison, in a black pit with straight sides and no way of climbing out. There was a little light up at the top, but there was no way I was going to reach it.

I would go into bookshops and I *had* to look at books and read about cancer, even though I knew that they would say that the prognosis was very poor. I could not help myself. I found a book by Lorna St Aubyn called *Today is a Good Day to Die*, which was written to help people cope with facing death. Part of me was thinking, 'I should read this book' and part of me was saying, 'But you're not going to die, you mustn't, you can't die'. It was a terrible conflict between the knowledge that I was going to die and the fact that I didn't want to die. And what could I do about it? Nothing. It was almost as if I had to keep reinforcing my negativity. I had to keep on punishing myself with 'you're going to die, you're going to die, you're going to die, you're going to die'.

I started on chemotherapy, one pill a day, and injected myself with interferon three times a week. It made me feel as if I had raging flu. Edward arranged for somebody to clean and do the ironing and washing and the mundane things. Friends and neighbours rallied around to keep the house going because I was unable to cope at all. I spent most of my time in bed in the depths of despair. Having previously had a mask of control, suddenly I had people looking at me with pity. That was very hard to take. I didn't want people to feel sorry for me. I didn't want their pity. Before, when friends had tried to do things for me, I'd always played the martyr and refused. I had hated accepting things from others. Suddenly the situation had changed, and it was as if I was giving up some of my control. I was having to let people help me, because I felt so ill and weak. People coming into the house to help out was a very difficult thing for me – accepting other people's love, imagining that people would want to do things for me. Such were my feelings of worthlessness.

On the tenth day I was starting to feel nauseous. I would spend hours vomiting but not bringing anything up, dreadful continual retching. It wasn't bad enough that I had cancer and was going to die, but I was inflicted with this awful treatment on top of it. Plus I was having to travel by train to St Lucy's. I had to walk through the meat market where the men had bloodstained aprons, seeing dead bodies of animals and breathing in the smell of blood. It was grotesque to walk through the stench. Then sitting in the waiting room with all these sad grey people fed my negativity even further. Somebody should have put a notice up saying *All hope dies here*. It was a place of no hope. The doctors and nurses were all so damn cheerful, but I soon learned that they were like that only as long as you played the passive role. If I played their game, they would deliver love and comfort and warmth, not otherwise. They wanted the power in *their* hands.

It brought back memories of my sister who had died of cancer when she was forty-eight, not much older than I was. At the time my brother-in-law decided that she shouldn't be told what she had got. I would go into the hospital, and she'd say, 'I've got cancer, haven't I? I have, haven't I?' and I had to say, 'No! of course you haven't.' I can remember doing that and being unable to look at her. Now I understand how appalling it is to be dishonest at that time, how awful it is for the person who is ill. How can they cope with their own feelings if everyone around them is evading the issue? How cruel it is not to tell them. The evasion of eye contact is a terrible thing. It must isolate them so much. I can remember looking at my sister and thinking, 'These words are coming out of my mouth but it's not what I'm thinking.' It was horrible.

I was in a very bad way emotionally. I was shot to pieces. It was as if I had retreated from life.

8

Then a friend of mine who knew that I was in a desperate state told Edward that her own GP, Dr John, now retired from his practice, was good at helping people in my situation. Did Edward think that I would see him? By now, Edward was at desperation point: because I couldn't cope, he couldn't cope, and neither could the children. It's strange how we mirrored each other. It was a vicious circle in which we were all passing despair on to each other.

'I don't know if she will,' he said, 'because she's withdrawn from life.'

'Here's his number anyway, and he'll speak to her if you call him.'

I will never know why I did call him. Knowing the state I was in, I am surprised I did. I don't remember the moment of decision. It was more out of sheer desperation than anything else. A cry for help.

I telephoned him. He had this wonderfully calm voice and I was immediately drawn to him. He made an appointment for me to go and see him. I'd only been taking the chemotherapy drug for a week or so, and wasn't feeling too ill. He lived only a mile up the road.

As soon as I saw him, I felt there was something special about him, something about his presence that was very reassuring. He struck me as wise and at one with the world. I felt safe with him, partly because he was a doctor – even though I hate the power figure now – and I felt I could trust him.

That first evening I cried the entire time, for at least an hour and a half. He sat there and listened while I poured out all this stuff between the sobs: my fear, my desperation that I was going to die. Because he was a doctor, I was asking him if he thought there was any hope, thinking was he going to give me the miracle cure. He just listened as I poured out my agony and grief. I felt a bit better for having shared it with a stranger, someone who just sat there and wasn't emotionally involved or judgemental, just a compassionate listener. Part of me was asking what difference talking to this man was going to make to anything, but somehow it was comforting.

I had taken that first step in going to see him. Even though I was thoroughly scared, I had made that first move. At the time I felt only complete despair, but somehow I was drawn back, so I arranged to go and see him a couple of days later. I was much calmer the second time. He asked me about my family and my life, so we started to talk about my childhood. At the end of it

all – it was very general stuff – he suggested trying hypnotherapy.
I agreed.

By then I was entering my second week of chemotherapy, and
starting to feel nauseous and tired. I could hardly get out of bed,
I was so tired. It was as if my body had ground to a halt. I was
heaving and retching. The hospital said that sometimes it affected
people like that but that I should just carry on.

Then one night I woke up. I don't remember much about it, but
apparently I was having hallucinations: there were spiders in the
bed and they were crawling all over me. I was hysterical. Edward
phoned St Lucy's in a panic saying that I was in a really bad way.
It was one o'clock in the morning and they told him to bring me
in. They kept me in for two or three days, and stopped all the
chemotherapy. I found out from Dr John afterwards that hallucinations are a sign that the lining of the brain is being irritated.

They kept me in. That has to have been one of the worst
experiences of my life.

9

I was put in a cancer ward with other women who had either
lymphoma or leukaemia, including quite a young girl of eighteen
or nineteen who sat praying with her Bible all the time. There was
a woman in the bed diagonally across from me who was in a really
bad way with lymphoma. Her legs were swollen with oedema and
she had a drip in her arm. She was obviously dying and I thought,
'I don't want to die like this'. They were all walking around with
their frames, with chemicals dripping into them. When they sat
down, they took their wigs off and they were bald. I was lying
there thinking, 'My God, this is what is going to happen to me.
This is how I am going to die.'

They all seemed so cheerful. Some of them were in dreadful
pain, the others would take off their wigs and go out to the toilet
for a smoke and a can of Coke. Nobody told them that they
should be looking after their bodies. It was as if they were saying,
'You haven't got much time left, so go and do what the hell you
like. Smoke yourself to death, eat and drink what you like

because it's not going to make any difference whatsoever to the outcome.'

Those few days had a profound effect on me. It brought home to me what was going to happen to me. That was the progression of the disease; that was how it was going to be.

While I was in there, I was introduced to the Professor, the head of the department. He was charm itself, the stereotypical consultant. A very short, dapper little man, always wearing a bow tie, he peered at people over the top of his bifocal spectacles. Wherever he went, he had an entourage following along behind. He was God personified as far as they were concerned.

He came in to see me the second day that I was in there for observation. He was the only one in a suit; all the others had their white coats on, so he stood out. He came sweeping in. I was lying there, me, a person, and he looked at them and said, 'This is a very interesting case here.'

Nothing to do with *me*; I was just a slab of meat lying there. I was an 'interesting case' because I was having all these strange reactions to the drugs. I was not going by the book. So they all came and had a prod and a look and I thought, 'This is what it is going to be like. For whatever time I've got left.'

With hindsight, all these things were contributing to my desperation to find an answer. Maybe it was the thing that pushed me to finding one.

When I came out of hospital, I went along to Dr John for the third session. We tried some hypnotherapy. I lay on a couch in his study looking at a crystal on top of a tall cabinet. He was sitting behind me. He darkened the room so that the crystal became the focal point as it shimmered in the corner.

'I want you to focus on the crystal and I want you to listen to my voice.'

I had never experienced hypnosis before, and was quite sceptical about it. I don't know what I had expected, but I was totally aware of what was going on and I found that strange. I felt very relaxed. He started to tell me this story about going down through a lane and opening a gate and going into a beautiful meadow. In one part there was a stream, and in another a cave, and another part had swampy ground which was not easy to walk on, and there was also a path leading up a hill. We went into the meadow and he told me about all the different parts of it.

'Where would you like to go? Would you like to go into the cave? Would you like to go down by the stream?'

'No, I would like to go up the hill.'

So we went up the hill with him guiding me. I was really anticipating getting to the top! It's a funny thing with hypnosis: it's only someone telling you a story in a relaxed state, but I wanted to see what was happening and what would come next.

We got to the top, and he said, 'Now you can look out over the top. What can you see?'

'Nothing.'

So he brought me back down the hill and we came out again. He told me later that the fact that I had chosen the hill meant that I wanted to find something. It was significant that I hadn't chosen the cave.

We tried the same imagery again the next time, but instead of bringing me down, he said, 'I want you to turn round and come down, and as you are walking you can see that someone is laying out a picnic in the meadow. You can't see who it is because they've got their back to you. You don't know who it is but they are waiting for you to share a picnic.'

He brought me down the hill. The sun was shining and the grass felt warm under my feet. I was getting closer and closer and looking forward to sharing this picnic. As I got closer, he said, 'The person is turning round, and you can see who it is.'

As he turned round, I saw it was my brother.

I had this enormous flashback from the past. I started to sob hysterically. He stopped, and switched the light on, and waited for me, but I couldn't stop.

'Who was it?'

I couldn't tell him at first. I was beside myself. Then I said, 'It was my brother.'

He didn't ask me any more.

I arrived home and Edward said, 'What on earth is the matter?'

I had gone out in a reasonable state, and come back almost hysterical. I couldn't tell him. I went to bed and I cried and I cried – it was as if there was forty years of misery inside me. I could not stop. It wasn't like the crying I'd done when I was told I was going to die; this was a deep, gasping sobbing, right from the depths.

Edward was really worried. He was in bed beside me and all night there was this sobbing, sobbing, sobbing. It must have been three or four o'clock in the morning, when suddenly it all came out.

I said to him, 'My brother raped me.'

10

I was still visiting St Lucy's at this point. On sending me home, they'd said that they were going to stop the treatment, give my body a chance to recuperate, and then embark on a different type of chemotherapy. I would lose my hair this time, but it wasn't going to make me feel ill like the other treatment.

Just before I was due to go back to the hospital, both my legs turned a dark damson colour from the knee to the ankle, a deep wine-stain colour. I called my GP. One of his partners came out and she looked at my legs with horror.

'We will send the nurse round and you must have a blood test immediately.'

When I asked her if she thought it was the chemotherapy, she said, 'Well, that stuff's like drinking a bottle of bleach.'

When I repeated that to my GP, he was furious with her. He was absolutely livid.

A nurse was sent round and took some blood. Within two hours, there was a frantic knocking on the door. My GP was standing on the doorstep.

'I've just got the results of your blood test. There is something really bad going on.'

'Why? What's happening?'

'It's full of allergy cells. It's very, very bad.'

I'd had a huge allergic reaction, my immune system was fighting itself and things were going seriously wrong.

The doctor phoned St Lucy's from the house and told them what had happened. It was agreed that they would give me a huge shot of steroids. So I was given an injection, and a large bottle of steroids to take.

What had happened was that the chemotherapy had damaged the capillaries and the arteries – when she said it was like drinking a bottle of bleach she meant that it makes holes in them. That's the bit they don't tell you; that's the bit that's glossed over. Blood was leaking out through the capillaries which was why my legs had turned a horrendous crimson colour.

They decided to take more blood and see what was happening. Steroids, they said, would sort the problem out.

Meantime I was still going back to see Dr John. We tried some more hypnotherapy, but I couldn't remember everything; I had a block. I remember that I had been frightened, I'd had a bad dream because my eldest sister, the one who died of cancer, used to frighten me. I was younger than her, by eighteen years. I was a very nervous child and was always having nightmares. She used to get enormous pleasure out of deliberately frightening me. Knowing what I have found out since, there was an enormous amount of resentment towards me that I didn't understand as I was growing up. She was the eldest sister, the second child. My brother Jake's room was across the corridor from mine and I had gone in there, frightened by my nightmare. I was scared, and he told me to get into bed with him, and then I couldn't remember anything.

Under hypnotherapy, Dr John would take me into different rooms: I would choose a door and open it, but then there would be nothing inside the door. I was throwing up blocks; the unconscious wasn't prepared to let me reclaim the memory.

I had been meant to be going back to St Lucy's, but I kept putting them off. They wanted me to start back on the treatment, but I kept saying, 'I can't go back on it, my body's not ready.'

It was as if I was stalling for time. I didn't know what else I was going to do, but I knew I had to give myself a bit of a breathing space. Having been very charming and nice, they started to get a bit cross with me because I wasn't doing what I was supposed to be doing. It was early November before I got them to agree that, because of the problem with my legs and the steroids, I could wait until after Christmas to recommence the chemotherapy.

By now it must have been the ninth or tenth visit to Dr John. We had been trying various things but without success. After that first revelation in the meadow, I was feeling an enormous amount of energy from somewhere. All the emotional energy that had been repressed was suddenly released. For the first time I was starting to get back into the driving seat. I wasn't totally in control, but I was wanting to get there.

Then the most amazing thing happened. It was the thing that changed everything.

11

I went to see Dr John and when I lay on the couch he said, 'I'm going to try something different. We'll see if we can have a bit more success.'

Ever since I had started seeing him, I had felt drawn to him. I kept saying things like, 'I'm never going to be able to stop coming here to see you' and he'd say, 'You will. You will know when you don't need me any more. And you *won't* need me any more'. I kept thinking, 'He's just saying that to reassure me.'

He had given me a book to read called *The Causes and Prevention of Cancer* by Dr Levenson. It was about using the power of the mind, and explained how repressed feelings and not living life as who you really are can cause cancer. The book suggested that cancer was not a malfunction in our bodies in the normal sense, but rather was something that came from within us. It was the destruction of ourselves by ourselves for some explainable reason.

During this time I was was feeling more and more uneasy about my treatment, from the point of view that I felt I was going to die very soon if I carried on with the chemotherapy. My body was in a bad way. I knew that the end wasn't going to be very long if I carried on along that route. It infuriated me that Dr John wouldn't tell me what to do, particularly as he was a doctor. When I decided I wasn't going to have the chemotherapy, I asked him what he thought I should do. I was still very scared. He just said, 'Don't ask me.'

And he actually said to me at one point, 'We get the illnesses we need.'

I thought, 'What a swinish thing to say! How can anybody possibly *need* to have cancer?' But now I understand exactly what he meant.

That evening we went into relaxation. Instead of going into a meadow, he said, 'You are in a desert. It is very, very hot and you are barefoot. You can feel the very hot sand under your feet. Over in the distance you can see a pyramid. You are going to walk over to the pyramid.'

I was walking through the sand in the intense heat and I could feel the sun on my head and my feet. I walked closer and closer to the pyramid, and when I got there I went inside. There was a big door in the side, and steps going down right into the heart of the pyramid, with big flaming torches on the wall lighting the path.

'I want you to start going down the steps.'

I went down and he said, 'You are going deeper and deeper into the pyramid.'

I went down, deeper and deeper.

'As you come round this corner, you are going to see a huge idol standing there, with a big gem in its head, shining very bright, very beautiful. That gem is your virginity. I want you to reach up and claim it and take it back. Are you doing that?'

'Yes, I'm reaching up now, and I'm taking it. I've pulled it out.'

'As you've pulled it out, the idol is crumbling, and as it crumbles, you will see that it's got feet of clay.'

'Yes, I can see that.'

I don't know what happened then. I went into a very deep hypnotic state. I have no idea what happened at that point. But some time later – and I don't know how long it was – I suddenly became aware that I was lying on the couch. I looked up and saw Dr John sitting at his desk facing me, which was not where he usually sat. He was writing. I must have made a noise. He looked up and said, 'Ah! you're back.'

'What happened?' I asked.

'You tell me!'

'Well, I remember you telling me this story,' and I told him about when the idol crumbled and I saw his feet of clay. I asked what had happened next.

'Your subconscious knows what happens next.'

'Aren't you going to tell me?'

'No. You'll remember when you need to. But it's not important for you to know – because you *do* know.'

I remember feeling irritated, to say the least, that he wouldn't tell me. Very irritated!

All I can say is that whatever happened at that moment transformed me. It was as if someone had switched on a power supply. If you can imagine the life source, it was as if someone had turned it on. Suddenly it was flowing through me. It's extraordinary. I wish I knew the mechanisms of what happened. I don't know, and I don't know if he really knows. I touched something when I went into that state, and what it was I don't know.

I only saw him once more after that – which is extraordinary considering that I had been thinking that I could never live without having this man as my mentor. Suddenly I didn't need him any more.

It was a miracle. I think about it now sometimes and think, yes, it really was a miracle. Something happened which my subconscious knows, but my conscious mind doesn't know. He knows, because of what he saw, but for whatever reason decided not to tell me.

I felt that it was a miracle that everybody could experience, if they could just have the opening. I was very lucky that this person came along just as I needed him, a man who lived only a mile down the road. It was the watershed of the whole thing. I never looked back.

12

I was sure that now, whatever was going to happen, I wasn't going to die. All I had to do was go where life took me and it was all going to be all right. I was absolutely adamant about that. I was confident, I was full of myself. I must have been very irritating to other people when I think back on it!

Friends said that the transformation was unbelievable. From the person who had given up, totally unable to cope with anything, I had suddenly become this really irritating, rather arrogant woman who thought she had the answer to life!

I had got rid of a big burden that had been weighing me down, and once I had done it, I had a *huge* surge of emotional energy. It was as if I had been tired all my life.

Dr John told me, 'The amount of energy you were using to keep the lid on this stuff has been released. Suddenly it is available to you.'

From then on I was so different from how I had been. It was a sort of miracle. The amazing thing was the effect it had on the people around me. I was then able to tell my children that I'd got cancer: I said, 'It's all right, I'm not going to die,' but this time I meant it. Suddenly they weren't frightened any more. I think they thought secretly, 'My God, it's turned her brain, it's part of the illness, she's suddenly gone potty.' But I found this enormous confidence and faith in myself, which I hadn't had before. Ever.

I think that we've all got a bit of God in us. I reached that whatever-it-was, and it told me that I just had to believe in myself. It sounds very simplistic, but these things *are* simple. It really was that simple.

I bought a health magazine and read a little piece in it about a weekend seminar for cancer sufferers. I decided to go. The other woman on the course was the total opposite to me. She was at the denial stage. She had a huge lump in her breast and had not dealt with it at all. She wouldn't even go and have it looked at. But she knew what it was. The leader talked to us about how to get the fear out of cancer. But I had just *done* that! He was slightly amazed at me. Here was this woman actually saying, 'I've got cancer, whoopee! Isn't it wonderful? Isn't it great?' It was a strange time.

His main theme was about getting fear and anger out of the system, thumping pillows and all that, but I was fairly confident at this stage that I wasn't looking for the emotional answer. It was that day that I first heard about the Gerson therapy. He happened to mention diet, and talked about Gerson and his ideas, and I became quite interested. He told me they were explained in a book by Beata Bishop called *A Time to Heal*. This was mid-December.

I returned from the weekend, got hold of a copy of the book and read it. As I read, I thought, 'This is for me. I'd love to be able to do this.' But I knew that it would be very expensive: there was the cost of the flight to Mexico, plus the cost of staying in the clinic which was very high. The therapy took two years and was very costly. However, something was forming in my mind: I didn't know how I was going to do it, but I was sure it would save me if I could.

13

I'll take you back a little here. Our life was very ordinary. We lived in a small village, we were comfortably off, and on the surface everything seemed fine, but underneath it wasn't. I wanted to make the perfect little family, because I hadn't had one as a child, and I couldn't understand why it never was 'perfect'. I couldn't see that it was *me* that was the problem! When you are like that you are always blaming other people – it's always somebody else, it is never you. You are trying to find gratification and never taking responsibility for anything. It's one of the reasons that I was attracted to Edward, because he was able to take responsibility.

In 1988 Edward's mother had a breakdown and had to go into a nursing home. His father could not cope on his own and we would get constant phone calls from him telling us we had to come down (it was never 'could you?'). He just could not cope with her not being around. It wasn't as if he was short of money and couldn't go out to restaurants to eat, he just *wouldn't* because it would upset his life too much. Edward was the only child, so the burden was very much on him. We spent our weekends rushing up and down the motorway. In the summer of 1989 we went away for a week's holiday and we got a phone call from his father saying we would have to come back as he couldn't cope!

In the end he asked if he could come and stay with us. We decided the best thing was to put Edward's parents' flat up for sale, move his mother to a nursing home near us and bring his father to live with us. This was in October 1989.

My father-in-law was a very domineering man, and very set in his ways. My mother-in-law was totally submissive to him. He would only have to say, 'Nancy! get so and so,' and she would be running up and down for him. They were quite well off and because Edward was the only child they were always very generous towards him, although his father was the sort of man who believed in making children save up for things so he didn't overindulge him. It would always be, 'Here's your birthday present and I want you to buy such-and-such with it'. Edward had never kicked balls around with his father, yet his parents took him off to foreign places on holiday. They were religious people, committed Christians, and in Edward's teens they insisted that he went to church with them. He rebelled and there was quite a conflict. Arthur was not an easy man.

Having him live with us was a disaster. Arthur lived by routine: meals were at set times and you had to have three courses at lunch. Nancy had waited on him hand and foot, but I had three young children. He couldn't understand that I just didn't have the time. Life was terrible. I began to feel more and more stressed. If I had a friend round, he would sit with us. If we went into another room, he'd come and sit there. Once I was in the kitchen with a girlfriend and he came in and said, 'You won't forget my lunch in ten minutes will you?'

Lunch had to be on the table at one o'clock, supper had to be at seven, and breakfast was at eight. He knew that Edward and the children had to go out in the mornings, yet he would go in the bathroom at the peak time, when everyone was trying to get ready. He didn't feel that his life should alter for anyone.

I had always been this negative, unable-to-cope sort of person. The fact that I had said I would have him live with us was typical of me. I knew I didn't really want to, but I'd spent all my life doing things that other people had told me to do rather than what I wanted to do. I knew that life was going to be hell but I still did it, because I was the eternal martyr.

Then Nancy had a slight stroke and started to develop early stages of dementia. Arthur went to see her regularly, but then one day he had a blackout at the wheel of his car. He was over eighty and after that it was decided that he shouldn't drive again. This put a greater burden on me, because I now had to ferry him around. Then he had a fit, and then another fit. We knew that we couldn't continue with all of us in our tiny house, but he refused to go into the nursing home with Nancy. People there were quite sick and had strange habits and he didn't want to be among them. It was an awful stress, but one that I had brought on myself. After about three months I said to Edward, 'I can't cope with this any more.'

So just after Christmas, at the start of 1990, we decided we would have to move house.

Our problem was that the old house was small, and there was no escape for any of us, so we agreed to look for something larger where Arthur could have an annexe to himself, and just have meals with us. He wanted us to find a big enough house so that he and my mother-in-law could be self-contained, and I very stupidly agreed. I don't know why I did, but I did. I knew that Edward's mother was never going to be well enough to come out of the nursing home, but he believed it, so I went along with it, which was typical of me then.

I had this stupid idea that once we moved, all my problems

would be solved and everything would be all right. In a way, that was true, but not in the way I thought! We moved in March 1990, into the house we are living in now, with my father-in-law. The house was in a terrible state and needed masses doing to it. Arthur was to have a part of it with his own sitting room, bedroom and bathroom, and just have meals with us. It wasn't an ideal house, but we were desperate by this point. So not only did I have the stress of Arthur living with us, I'd also gone through all the major stress of moving house. It was probably the straw that broke the camel's back for me.

14

We had only been in the house two weeks when Arthur had a couple of blackouts. He started to be incontinent, and his fits frightened the life out of the children. I was really stressed by this time. Then he suddenly said, 'I'm going to the nursing home.'

Just like that. We sat and looked at him in amazement.

'We have only just moved here!'

'I don't care. I want to go in the nursing home.'

He was one of those people who once he had made up his mind it had to be done immediately. 'Get on to the nursing home, get me a place, it's all got to happen *now*.'

Part of us was relieved that he was going, but the other part was absolutely furious that we had gone through this stressful move, and were living in a house that needed God knows what doing to it. It had taken ages to find it and we had only bought it because we were desperate. It was close to the motorway and was not our ideal house. We were very angry with him, but there was no dissuading him. He was adamant.

So we arranged with the nursing home that he could have a room next to Nancy's. He went in in April 1990, a month after we moved. We carried on seeing them there, going back and forth to visit the home all the time. Suddenly we had acquired *two* sick parents. But there was no reason why they shouldn't live for years: they were being cared for and we were visiting them every weekend.

I had my diagnosis in September 1990, but we never told them that I was ill. I had heard about the Gerson therapy and was thinking how I would love to have it, but there was no way we could possibly afford it. Then suddenly, in January 1991, a few weeks after I first heard about the Gerson therapy, my mother-in-law's health worsened. She became very thin, got a cold which went to her chest and finally got pneumonia. They moved Arthur in with her and they lay there holding hands. Despite his domineering ways, he was devoted to her. Then a few days later they phoned Edward at the office to say that she was very poorly. He dashed over there to be with her when she died.

I hadn't spoken very much to Edward about the Gerson therapy. I didn't want to put any more pressure on him because he was very stressed. At least I was feeling much happier in myself which was better for him. But now I started to say to him that I would really like to have this therapy, although I knew there was no way we could afford it.

Three weeks later we had a phone call to say that Edward's father was dying. After Nancy died, he never spoke again. He had Parkinson's disease and there had been a slow deterioration while he had been in the nursing home. He was in a wheelchair by then. By the time Edward got there he had died.

There we were at the end of February 1991 and they had suddenly gone, one after the other. Edward said to me, 'This therapy you've been talking about, we can do it!'

Suddenly here was the answer to all our problems. We both had this insight that his parents' death was somehow a gift to me to carry on living. We both felt that very strongly, yet until then I would never have thought that Edward was the kind of man to have these insights.

'But,' he said, 'there's going to be a problem about the money because it's going to be some months before we get probate.'

I felt almost guilty that we were saying, 'Whoopee! We can go and do this thing' when his parents had just died. I felt bad, but it was at this point that we started to see the connections. We started to see that since what had happened with Dr John, all these so-called coincidences had started to happen. I can remember saying that I felt as though I was being pushed down a path since meeting Dr John, I had had this very strong feeling of being guided. Edward didn't regard this as at all fanciful. We both felt that they died to enable me to do this, and if I didn't do it, then it was madness. He didn't even ask me much about what the therapy entailed! He just saw it as a way out. If this was what it had to be, then this was the way we were going to go.

Since just before Christmas of 1990 I had wanted to have this therapy, but had thought there was no way we could afford it. Then just two months later, suddenly we could. It was almost as if they died to save me.

15

Then lo and behold, another coincidence: a girlfriend of mine, Caroline, who I used to share a flat with but hadn't seen for some years, phoned me out of the blue. She's Helen's godmother and I hadn't seen her since 1982. I had spoken to her when I was diagnosed in September, and had told her then that I had cancer. Now we spoke again.

'I've read about this Gerson therapy and I want to go to Mexico and do it,' I told her.

'What about Edward and the children?'

'Yes, that's one of the things that's bothering me.'

'Well, I've got the answer. Why don't they come and stay with us in California? Then they can come and see you in Mexico.'

So they arranged all the technicalities. Edward's father died on 21 February and we were faced with having to wait for probate. Tony, Caroline's partner, told us not to worry, and just gave us the money. He paid all the bills in the clinic and yet he hardly knew us at all. We paid him back when the money came through later, but in all he lent us many thousands of pounds. They were wonderful.

Edward never once asked how much all this was going to cost. Money had always been a security blanket for me. Parts of my old patterns would surface now and again and I would wonder if we ought to be spending all this money. It was the feeling of not deserving it: why should anyone want to give this to me? I found it amazing that he should be willing to do this to save my life. By the same token, he found it amazing that I should think that he wouldn't want to. He would say, 'For goodness sake! you can get money at any time!'

Because he had grown up with the security of material things, it wasn't something that bothered him. Money was something you could accumulate again. Another man might have stopped and thought of all the reasons why we shouldn't do it, but he didn't: he had seen me being snatched away, and suddenly here was a chance of my coming back again.

He was fantastic. He willingly said, 'It's all yours to use.' He didn't *have* to do that. I thought it was wonderful. In view of my family background, it was an enormous comfort to me to know that somebody was willing to do that for me. He was so generous, and not only in a material way. He was really supportive. I now know lots of other Gerson patients whose relatives were against them having the therapy which must have made it even more of an uphill battle. Edward also had a sense of relief, because he too felt very negative about the chemotherapy and in some ways he was glad that I had voluntarily said, 'I want to follow this other path'. He just felt that I knew what I was doing. To have his faith as well was a real support and strength.

Before I heard about the Gerson therapy, I had been referred to a specialist in nutritional medicine, Dr Allan, to talk about my diet and what I could do to help myself. My own GP and Professor Stellart at St Lucy's had told me that nutrition had nothing what-soever to do with cancer: it was a total waste of time. They weren't prepared to give me any advice, so I had to find it elsewhere.

I had a series of tests to find out what I was deficient in. It was found that I was low in zinc and red-cell magnesium, which I later discovered are two of the crucial minerals for detoxification. If you are lacking in them, the body can't get rid of toxins.

Dr Allan was very sympathetic about my condition, but when I told him that I was going to have the Gerson therapy he advised me very strongly against it. He said he had never yet seen a successful Gerson patient and that I was embarking on an ex-tremely risky venture. One of the reasons that he didn't agree with it was that there was no protein for the first twelve weeks. 'Your body can't survive without protein,' he said. Vegetable protein is not enough, particularly for a sick body that is fighting cancer. But much later he actually admitted, 'If I had melanoma, I'd go on the Gerson therapy.'

But he did tell me that you have to be very careful taking supplements, because they put substances into the body in a form which it cannot readily use. A healthy body can utilize them, but with cancer it's too late. The body isn't able to use them in tablet form, and the tumour gobbles them and gets bigger and fatter. One of the reasons why treatments based on high doses of vitamins are not that successful is because the B vitamins are known to promote tumour growth. So while people are having chemotherapy and their bodies become even more depleted, they have to be very careful about vitamin supplements because some of them promote the growth. It's fine taking supplements if you are *not* sick, as the body can utilize them. But if you are already ill, it's a bit like swallowing a ball-bearing: it goes in one end and out the other and the body isn't able to absorb anything from it.

16

The Gerson therapy is a scientific dietary treatment. The digestive tract, Gerson said, is the first thing to break down with cancer patients who are not able to absorb nutrients. He prescribed freshly-pressed juices which go straight into the bloodstream, so that the body is able to extract the nutrients without breaking anything down. So it doesn't matter that the gut is in a poor condition if the body is able to absorb those nutrients direct. People who spend £200 a week on vitamins are wasting their money and time. The body is not able to use them and all they are doing is feeding their tumours, which become bigger and bigger, whereas the body is able to use the wonderful nutrition in the form of fresh juices.

Gerson believed that disease occurs in the body – not just cancer, but arthritis, diabetes, and other conditions – when the body becomes toxic. It spends so much time dealing with this toxicity that it becomes more and more depleted. He believed that if you detoxify the body and rebuild the immune system, giving the body the things it needs to do so, then the immune system can do its job to defend the body against invasion.

As a medical student, Gerson suffered terribly from migraines and was told it was something he would have to put up with. However, he wasn't prepared to, so he experimented with his diet and found that when he ate just fresh organic fruit and vegetables he no longer had migraines. He then started to use this diet on his migraine patients. He happened to have one patient who had skin tuberculosis (lupus) as well as migraine, who came to him and said that both his migraines and the lupus had gone. Gerson could not believe it, because there was no known cure at that time. Out of 450 lupus patients who tried Gerson's therapy, 436 were cured. So it became standard therapy for skin TB.

His cure became quite well known so people started coming to him asking him to cure cancer. He said that he couldn't, but some people whose cancer was terminal were prepared to try it. That was how the therapy started. But then he found that patients were dying of liver failure: once the body started to release and detoxify, the liver couldn't cope with the sudden discharge of all the toxins into the bloodstream. So he started to use enemas.

Coffee enemas originated in the First World War. Toward the end of the war, when drugs were scarce, and there were many soldiers ill and in pain, they used ordinary enemas to help control pain. Enemas remove circulating toxins and thus reduce pain. How coffee enemas came about was as bizarre as this: the nurses would be making pots of coffee for the doctors to keep them going, and they noticed the perky effect that coffee had. So they would tip it into the patients' enema buckets. That was how it started! If you just drink coffee it has a different effect on the gut, but when it is absorbed by the haemorrhoidal veins, the bile ducts open up and toxins in the liver are swept out.

There were times later when I would wake up with terrible headaches, hardly able to open my eyes because my system was so toxic. I'd take a coffee enema and the headache would be gone. It was incredible how it worked! The amount of toxins you must have when breaking down a tumour is enormous, and coffee enemas take that pressure off the liver.

Gerson was allowed to practise in Germany where his theories were accepted. There's much information in German medical journals from that time showing how huge numbers of people were cured of skin TB for which there was no cure at that time. They were all cured by using his dietary methods. He fled to the USA as the Nazis gained power in the thirties, but his work was outlawed by the American Senate in spite of its success. There was a huge push towards chemical treatments and radiation at that time, and the drug companies were lobbying for them. So much for 'freedom': nobody was allowed to choose between his treatment and the orthodox route. Thus Gerson was rejected by the medical establishment in the USA.

So it was only when he went to America that he became outcast from the profession – and because he was curing people! He had all the documentation to show that the people he had treated were dying, that the rest of the medical profession had failed to cure them. But the drug companies and the chemical companies stood to lose too much: they wielded enormous power and they would have none of him.

The object of the Senate hearings in 1946 was to raise money to pursue alternative cancer treatments. Gerson had all these files on people he had cured, people who were considered terminal by the orthodox practitioners. He presented these cases to the Senate hearings but was given no money. After that he was ostracized by the rest of his profession, and he died a very unhappy man. In Europe things had been different. When the medical profession found that his diet worked, they took it on board quite readily. If Hitler hadn't come to power and Gerson hadn't fled from Germany – he was a Jew – then maybe . . . but then that's speculation. Europeans have a much gentler approach to treating illness, especially in France and Germany where they are much more receptive to new ideas and where alternatives are accepted and incorporated into the mainstream. Gerson's ideas originated in Germany, and there are still a lot of alternative cancer therapies there. His medical training was considered at the time to be the best in the world.

Gerson told the Senate hearings his opinion of what cancer was:

> In my opinion cancer is not a problem of deficiencies in hormones, vitamins and enzymes, it is not a problem of allergies or infections with a virus or with any other known or unknown micro-organism; it is not a poisoning through some intermediate metabolic substance, or any other substance coming from an outside so-called carcinogenic substance. All these can be partial causative agents in men, contributing elements called secondary infections etc. Cancer is not a single cellular problem, it is an accumulation of numerous damaging factors combined in deteriorating the whole metabolism after the liver has been progressively impaired in its function.

Dr Allan warned me very strongly against opting for the treatment. I decided to do it anyway.

17

Since the autumn I'd had the negative onslaught of going backwards and forwards to hospital, constantly having blood taken –
it even got to the stage where they couldn't find any more veins
to use. The doctors would spend hours looking up and down my
arm trying to find one. It was an endless round of chemotherapy
and radiotherapy. People like Professor Stellart say, 'Oh, how
brave these people are.' I think, 'No, they're not brave; they are
somebody else's fool.' Sitting in the waiting room at St Lucy's
with these grey people was feeding my negativity. They were all
feeling like me, life's rejects, waiting to be processed down the
conveyor belt of death.

After my experience with Dr John, I had this new strength. I felt
I could do it all on my own, without Edward having to come with
me, and I didn't have to accept help from anyone.

I was meant to go back to St Lucy's in January for them to
embark on the chemotherapy. They had sent a letter to my GP:

DIAGNOSIS: Stage IV follicular lymphoma diagnosed September
1990.
I saw this lady in the clinic. Unfortunately she had to stop taking
chlorambucil and interferon after three weeks of treatment, predomi-
nantly because of nausea and vomiting with severe headaches, which
she ascribed to the chlorambucil. As her blood count had fallen
sharply, we observed her without further chemotherapy but she then
developed a widespread rash with the features of erythema multi-
forme for which you kindly prescribed oral steroids. The rash is now
settling, although she has some residual pruritis and it is our intention
to allow all the side-effects to settle before making a further attempt
at treating her lymphoma, this time with cyclophosphamide and
interferon. On the positive side, her superficial lymph nodes have
diminished considerably in size since she started the treatment and
we still hope to achieve a worthwhile remission.

Unknown to them, such a lot had happened to me in that short
space of time. First, I thought I was immortal! Second, I had heard

about the Gerson therapy and was fired with enthusiasm for it.

I saw a different doctor who said he was going to give me a new chemotherapy drug. I asked him what side-effects it had. In view of what I had experienced, that seemed a perfectly legitimate question.

He looked at me and said, 'You don't get side-effects when you're dead.'

Bluntly. Just like that. He obviously thought, 'How dare this difficult woman ask what side-effects she was likely to have!' It was obviously designed to frighten me.

It made me so angry that I said, 'I'm not going to have it.'

'Just a moment.'

He went out, came back and said, 'Professor Stellart would like to see you.'

I was led into the inner sanctum. A patient who had dared to refuse their wonderful treatment. It sounds cynical but their attitude has made me like that. They are *so* closed-minded. If they had said, 'Look, we think you're making a big mistake, but it's your life and your decision', I could have accepted it, but it was, 'You stupid woman, how can you possibly know what's good for you? We are the doctors, we know what's good for you'. I find it amazing that they are so insensitive. There you are, going through this terrible trauma of a life-threatening illness and they treat you like this; it's appalling. They cut bits out or burn them off or bleach your system. You as a person don't exist. Not unless you are so full of tears that they have complete control over you.

But if you're not . . . This sudden transformation flummoxed them, and they thought, 'What the hell's going on? How do we handle this?' From their point of view I can see that it must have been an amazing sight: from grovelling and saying, 'I'll do anything you say', to the opposite extreme.

Sister was in there as well and she looked at me as if to say, 'How can somebody answer this man back? How can anyone question this all-powerful God?'

When I told the Professor I'd had hypnotherapy, he said, 'That is ridiculous! It couldn't possibly make anyone better. It has nothing to do with it – your thoughts are in a different compartment. They don't affect what goes on in your body.'

I said, 'I'm going to do the Gerson therapy.'

'Is your husband here?'

I was incensed.

'Perhaps he can talk some sense into you.'

In other words, you are just some stupid woman, how can you possibly have any control over your life? We need to speak to your husband.

All these comments that were designed to put the fear of God in me had the opposite effect. I thought, 'If only he knew the effect he is having!'

'What is this . . .?' and he deliberately mispronounced Gerson as Gurzon. I'll swear that he knew about it because the year before, two well-known oncologists from London had gone out to Mexico and their evaluation of the therapy was written up in *The Lancet* (see Bibliography). I can't believe that he didn't know about it. He deliberately did that to put it down.

'I'm going and that's it.'

'How long does this "Gurzon therapy" take?'

'Eighteen months.'

At the time I thought that was correct, and I didn't realize that it was going to take me longer than that.

'You'll be dead long before then.'

'Well, we'll see, won't we?'

I can remember sitting there smiling, because he was so angry, and I could see that I was needling him. I must have had a smirk on my face.

'I'm glad you think it's funny!'

I couldn't help myself. It was the naughty child in me flouting the authority figure.

I got up and left.

I then got a letter from him saying that if I wanted to increase my life-expectancy, I'd better have chemotherapy immediately:

I hope that you are continuing to feel well. I write to give you details of your illness so that you can present them to the staff at the Gurzon clinic.

When you first came to see me, you were found to have an illness called follicular lymphoma involving the glands and bone marrow. You were treated with a combination of chlorambucil at a dose of 10mg daily and alpha-interferon 2000,000 units/m^2 subcutaneously three times a week (the indication for the treatment was backache). Unfortunately by the end of two weeks' therapy you were feeling rotten with aches and pains all over exacerbated by the interferon injections. As a result of this, all treatment was stopped. You subsequently developed a rash which was ascribed to the chlorambucil.

We decided that the best thing to do was to treat you with cyclophosphamide. All the while the glands were getting smaller. Not surprisingly you were not enthusiastic to restart the treatment, despite the fact that we suggested an alternative treatment to go with the interferon which would not have been so upsetting.

Although you remained well throughout the beginning of this year, the glands have now come back and my present advice is very strong – that you should have further treatment as the likelihood is that this will increase your life-expectancy. Obviously I would be delighted to be proved wrong and would be very interested to see how you get on with the Gurzon diet. Do make sure you make a trip into the desert and come and see me when you come back. If you do change your mind, I would be delighted to see you sooner.

I thought, 'Is this man for real? One moment he's saying you're dead if you don't take the drugs, and the next minute he's telling me to make a sightseeing trip into the desert, it's a wonderful sight . . . What does he think I'm going to do out there?'

From then on it all swept along. I was in a state of euphoria. My experience with Dr John had given me an inner strength that was greater than the fear of the cancer. It carried me along. There was so much activity in those early months of the year: trying to raise money for the therapy, then Edward's parents becoming ill and dying, then making all the arrangements for the family. On 27 March 1991 we left Gatwick and flew out to the States.

PART 2

Reprieve

Rather light a candle than complain about the darkness.

CHINESE PROVERB

18

We flew to Palm Springs. The children were very excited because they had never been to America. I felt apprehension and, fear mixed with a feeling that I was embarking on an amazing journey, a real adventure. I had always been terrified of flying, and suddenly I was going to have to fly a long way. I thought, this is ridiculous! Here I am, about to die, and I'm worried about a plane crash! The absurdity of the thought dispelled my fear.

We left Gatwick late and the plane was very crowded. I sat next to somebody who smoked the whole way across the Atlantic. There was nowhere to move to because the plane was so full. I felt awful, I looked grey and ill and arrived feeling really tired. Seeing the stretched limousines outside the airport felt like being on another planet. Caroline and Tony were there waiting to meet us.

We had decided to spend Easter with them before I went to the clinic. So I spent a lovely weekend with the children, watching them swimming in the pool, going to Disneyland, and going out to dinner. Sunday was my last night of eating normal food. We were woken on the Monday by poor Helen who had had a nightmare and came into the room very early in the morning, knowing I was going away that day. At this point I was very apprehensive about the clinic because I didn't know what to expect. A few months ago I'd only just been diagnosed, and so much had happened in such a short space of time. We set off after a very tearful goodbye. I wrote in my diary: 'Am I going to see them again? Am I going to come back?' I felt very upset, but I knew I had to do this if I wanted to get better.

Edward and I drove down to San Diego and parked the car, caught a bus to the border crossing, walked through, and got a cab to the hospital. From the affluent billionaires' paradise of California, we walked just a few yards into total poverty. There was netting all along the border and faces looking through to the other side. The Americans work so hard to keep out the Mexicans, who are desperate to get in to the riches on the other side.

The brochure said the clinic overlooked the Pacific, so I had this glamorous idea of what it was going to be like. It was a shock. The main roads in Mexico are dusty dirt tracks with huge pot-holes. The taxi was weaving in and out, and when we pulled up, we saw a converted motel called Del Sol. It was nothing like a hospital at all. When I saw it I said, 'I'm not going in there.' I started to think, 'What have I done? This is madness! How can a clinic be in a dump like this? I've come from this hi-tech institution called St Lucy's and here I am in this dirty, dusty place putting my life in the hands of who knows what.'

For a few minutes I was panic-stricken. It was just as well that Edward felt so positive about it.

'Come on, it'll be all right once we get inside.'

Within a very short time, my fears were banished. The nurses and all the staff were warm, kind people, and so positive. In contrast to the cancer ward in England which was full of fear, this place was full of hope. The Mexicans were friendly and smiling, and they chattered away to me in Spanish. I didn't understand a word, but because they were beaming at me it felt fine.

I was asked if I wanted a room with an ocean view. The view looked across the highway, a dusty track, to the beach and the ocean. Unlike California, with its clean sandy beaches and beautiful water, there were open pipes pumping sewage out. The beach was used as a rubbish tip. My room was clean, but very basic, with an enema couch and a toilet – everyone had to have their own because of the constant enemas. The Mexican sewage system is ancient, to say the least, and the strain on it must have been enormous. We were asked to flush the toilets as little as possible. I wrote in my diary, 'The hospital is not as nice as I had expected. Still, I'm not here to take in the sights!'

I had phoned Max Gerson's daughter Charlotte, from California to ask her details of the therapy.

'What have you got?' she asked me.

'Lymphoma, stage 4.'

'We've had a lot of success with lymphoma.'

It was wonderful after all the doom and gloom – she was full of confidence about her father's work which in turn filled me with confidence. The doctor's attitude, instead of the Professor's 'You do as I say; this is the progression of your disease and this is the way you'll do it', was suddenly 'It's all in your hands'. This is what Dr Gerson found, that the answer lies with *you*. It was an inspiring feeling. You may have someone to inspire you, and that is important – a key figure, a catalyst – but when it comes down to it, you have still got to do it yourself.

People there were saying, 'I arrived here and I had terrible pain and now it's gone.' There were lots of wonderfully hopeful stories. But in a way it was still like being in a tunnel – although this tunnel now had a light at the end of it. That is why I had got to keep digging into myself, because otherwise I was not going to get to that light.

They gave us lectures on *why* our bodies had succumbed to cancer, and what would happen when we started to detoxify. Somebody was actually telling us what was going on. Our bodies eliminate rogue cells all the time, so why are they suddenly allowed to grow unchecked? It's because our defences are not working properly; they are being used for some other purpose. So if you root out that cause, the body can fight the battle against cancer. All the body's energies are so consumed with whatever it is; that is why it's unable to defend itself.

I'm sure that's why cancer comes back after remission for lots of people, because the symptoms are dealt with but not the cause. The body's defences are still being consumed with other business. Dr John told me that the amount of energy needed to repress feelings is *phenomenal*. The key to the immune system, more than anything else, is what's going on in the mind. Either doctors don't see the connection, or they don't want to see it because all their expensive drugs would become redundant. It would take power away from the doctor if the individual were to take control.

I was in Mexico for three weeks. From day one, as soon as I arrived, it was straight on to thirteen juices a day: one orange juice, four green juices – lettuce, chard, green pepper, watercress (not particularly pleasant, rather bitter), five carrot and apple juices, and three carrot juices, plus five coffee enemas a day. Potassium was taken in the juices, we had acidoll before meals to stimulate our digestive juices and pancreatin with our meals to aid digestion. Thyroid tablets and lugol solution were given to speed up the metabolism, and we had vitamin B12 crude liver injections. The only fat we were allowed at this point was flax seed oil.

I was amazed at the cosmopolitan atmosphere in the clinic. There were Americans, Australians, lots of Germans, English, Japanese – all brought to one place in the hope that they were going to survive. The one consistent factor seemed to be the horror stories people could tell about orthodox doctors. All had undergone months of radiotherapy or chemotherapy, months of agony and fear, and at the end were told, 'Sorry, there's nothing else we can do'. The sad thing is that the Gerson therapy was always seen as a last resort. I was lucky compared to most people – two weeks of chemotherapy was all I'd had.

You could almost tell the patients who were going to survive and the ones who weren't. Those who complained constantly about the food ('how am I going to eat this for the next 18 months?') were so negative about it all that they had no chance. Then there were the others who really believed in it, as I did.

19

You have to eat lots of food on the Gerson therapy: people tend to think that it is a starvation diet. My own GP's notes said 'fasting'! However, it is just the opposite: because your body is in a bad way, you eat as much food as you can – the right sort of food. The last thing you must do is deprive your body of nourishment, because that is what it needs to fight the battle. Gerson's theory that the gut is the first thing to break down with cancer means that the body does not absorb nutrients, therefore it becomes weaker because it is not getting what it needs. So you detoxify the body, the immune system recharges, and then the body can deal with the disease.

Breakfast was a huge bowl of porridge made with water, with stewed fruit – prunes, dates, figs, raisins, sliced banana – and fresh orange juice. I could have a slice of special sour-dough bread, made without yeast, salt or fat, with a thin scraping of honey if I wanted it. And I drank lots of peppermint tea because it is soothing on the gut.

Lunchtime was a huge raw salad, with great bowls of lettuce, tomatoes, radishes and raw garlic to help ourselves from. The only thing we didn't eat was cucumber. We also had 'Hippocrates' soup made with celery, garlic, leeks, tomatoes, onions and potatoes, then jacket potatoes, vegetable casseroles, stuffed peppers, stewed asparagus – all cooked very slowly so that it is easy for the body to digest. The Gerson diet uses well-cooked vegetables with no water added, sealed and stewed slowly in their own juices, to aid the digestive process and to push things through.

The evening meal was a replay of lunch, and there was as much fresh fruit as you liked when you felt hungry. Day or night, they would bring to your room apples, oranges, bananas, mangoes, peaches, pears, papayas. I ate and ate and ate! The food was wonderful. Most of it came from just across the border in California. Food grown in the sun has a sweetness, and the vegetables and fruit were all organic. They tasted and looked wonderful. We were having all this solid food, plus thirteen juices, plus as much fruit as we could eat. Somehow I managed this enormous quantity of food easily!

Gerson believed that people are mistaken about the value of fasting: because your body is fighting something, you have to give it lots and lots of nutrition which it needs for the battle. However, a problem arises when people get very sick. When their in the final stages of a disease, one of the first things that goes is their appetite. Some people could only nibble tiny quantities of food; others had tumours in the gut and it was difficult to get food down, even though they were able to drink the juices. The green juice was the only thing that wasn't delicious, but as I drank it I made myself think of all the liquid energy that was going inside my body.

Now sometimes, if I have been out and am feeling tired, my eyes light on the juicer. I get a big bag of carrots out, juice them all and drink this huge glass of wonderful orange liquid. It's like Popeye with his spinach: you can feel it rushing to all the cells in your body and giving it lots of energy. It's a bit like that with the enemas – a lot of people use them in a psychological way, feeling that as they expel their enemas, all the negativity, the bad feelings, the old shit, are literally being expelled with them. The link between the nutritious juice going in, zooming to all the cells, and this enema carrying out the purging, had a very good effect on my emotional state.

It was so different from the hospital in England, where there was a false jollity, a mask that everyone was wearing over their fear. Instead of smoking, drinking Coke and eating rubbish, we were given beautiful food. The food I had in St Lucy's was grotesque: limp cornflakes with milk, and a piece of white pappy sliced bread spread with ghastly margarine. As I ate, it was as if my body was wondering what on earth it was supposed to do with it. What a difference to see this great trestle table in the dining room! You helped yourself to bowls piled high with jacket potatoes and huge colourful salads and soups and urns full of fragrant herbal teas. You only had to look at the food and it made you feel better! The horrible food in hospital had the reverse effect, but here the body felt excited about it, as though it was saying, 'Gosh, let me get at it! This is going to revitalize me!'

Lunch and dinner were always the same. For some people it was boringly monotonous, but I love salads and fruit and vegetables, so for me it was perfect. I had this vast appetite. My body could not get enough of this food. There were people sitting nibbling and eating minute portions and there was I, being almost gluttonous. I would go back and eat bowls and bowls of it. Salads, baked potatoes, corn on the cob, yams, beets cooked with potato and onion, whole onions cooked with sultanas. It was as if I was seeing food in a new light: it *did* matter what I put into myself. I had purged my emotional self with Dr John, now here was all this stuff that was going to help me purge my body.

Over the last few years, people have asked me how I can eat this food, but I've never had a problem with it. I love it, and even now I still live on it. I know that when it goes into my body, my body can do something with it; it's good energy. It has made me look at fruits and vegetables in a whole different way, with reverence and respect. They are beautiful things.

20

Once you have been taught the therapy, it is up to you to put it into practice yourself. With the Gerson therapy, the person doing the treating is *you*. If you have internal conflicts, there will always be a demon on your shoulder, your unconscious mind, telling you that you are going to fail and that you can't do it. However strong your desires are these conflicts will always come and slap them down and say, 'No, you're going to die'. These thoughts are always there, nibbling away at you. You have to get rid of them first: no matter how good and effective the Gerson therapy is – and I am sure that it could be one-hundred per cent effective

– you can't allow for people's own emotional conflicts, and many people sabotage their own progress.

The majority of people need support: I had Dr John. The Gerson therapy is half of the cure; the other half is your own internal work. The two together are very powerful although Charlotte Gerson would say that some people survive without looking at their emotional side. I would say that due to the nature of the Gerson therapy, you are forced, because you are confined so much, to look at those parts of yourself. The people that don't are the ones who don't make it. They are the ones who say they can't follow this diet, and what harm will it do if they eat so-and-so – they sabotage it because of their own inner demons. They then blame the therapy, so the success rate is difficult to evaluate, although they do have figures for melanoma which show a one-hundred per cent success rate after five years for stages 1 and 2, eighty-two per cent for stage 3a and seventy per cent for stages 3a and b combined – considerably higher than those reported elsewhere.

Charlotte Gerson can't understand why people get frightened. She gets exasperated, and people find that difficult to deal with: 'Just get on with it: do as I say and you'll be all right!' Her argument has always been that the Gerson therapy is enough in itself – it is such hard work that it's enough for most people to cope with. Personally I would like to see people dealing with their emotional problems *before* they start the Gerson therapy. The reason why people fail is because they haven't dealt with them. But then there's the question of time: if you are that ill, there isn't enough time. That's where hypnotherapy is such a valuable tool, because it's a short cut. I am sure that, having kept those things buried for forty-six years, if I'd gone into normal psychotherapy, I would have just talked around them, and never have got to the root cause.

Charlotte was very pleased that I had only had two weeks chemo and said to thank my lucky stars that my body reacted in the way it did. It was telling me something; it was saying, 'I don't like this'. The huge doses of steroids that they had given me had only suppressed my reactions and had driven the disease back inside the body. The doctor who first examined me said that, considering everything, I looked better than she had expected.

We all had in common the fact that we were fighting our disease – although I didn't think of it as a fight. By this stage, it was something I had embraced. You almost had to love it, put your arms around it and say, 'Yes, this is part of me, it's giving me something, it's telling me something and I haven't got to have a conflict any more, I haven't got to fight it. I've got to go with it, embrace it. I have to get rid of it, but not in an aggressive way, but in a loving, understanding way. That's how I'm going to get it to go.'

It's a bit like if you have a child who's being difficult or naughty: smacking isn't going to solve the problem; you've got to give it love and understanding, and then it will get better on its own.

I was embracing and loving the food, too. Some people hated the food and said they couldn't eat it, while I was loving it and eating vast quantities. Was it something about themselves that they hated that was reflected into their attitude to the food?

People would ask me how I could be so happy and cheerful. I had packed brightly coloured clothes and people would say it was a tonic just to look at me. But that was how I felt. Although my skin looked grey, this was a way of brightening myself up. Most other people didn't feel like doing that.

Love *does* conquer all, and if you do love this *thing* then your body will say, 'Yes! We can get rid of it'. I'm not at all sure about some of these visualization techniques where people are told to imagine that their cancer is some monster and that their lymphocytes are sharks devouring it. Some people find that effective, but it's really quite negative; it's not positively embracing the cancer, not seeing it as a separate bit of you but as part of you, as a little bit that's gone wrong. But you have to learn to love yourself first.

21

When Dr Sanchez first came to see me, she explained to me how the steroids had suppressed my reaction to the chemotherapy, but had not cured anything. She also asked me about my medical history. I told her that I hadn't had any periods since I'd had chemotherapy. I have never had them since. Instant menopause! I told her that I had had my tonsils out when I was eleven, and my appendix removed in 1984. She groaned.

'Why?' I said. 'Is that significant?'

'They cut out two vital parts of your immune system. The fact that your tonsils kept swelling as a child was because they were trying to fight something! So something else had to take the load. The appendix was the next one; it became overloaded and what did they do? Did they find out why these parts of your immune system became overloaded? No, they cut another lump of it out.'

I was horrified: as she was telling me this, I could see it all, yet nobody had said anything to me about it. Doctors don't tell you they are going to cut out a vital part of your immune system. It's 'Oh well, you don't need your appendix. You don't need your tonsils. You can live quite happily without them.' I was really angry that nobody had told me these things.

Dr Sanchez was very motherly, quietly spoken, soft and gentle.

'Oh, these Western doctors – they send us all these problems!' She sounded resigned. 'If only they had treated you differently.'

I thought, 'This is wonderful – somebody is actually telling me something.'

Once she had told me, it was all so clear.

I had my first coffee enema: I was full of gas. When you are extremely toxic and you take a coffee enema, the effect is quite disgusting. When the coffee hits a pocket of gas in the gut, it pushes it all out again. You lie there with this coffee trying to get past all the impacted stuff on the gut wall. It brought it home to me how furred-up your body becomes inside, and even a simple thing like getting some fluid up becomes an almost impossible task.

We then had a lecture from Charlotte Gerson. She is a strong personality, who believes that what her father discovered is written in tablets of stone. She is so positive, she gives you so much energy, she radiates it. She's very blunt, and tells people to jolly well believe in what they are doing. She's in her seventies and is a walking monument to her father's way of living. She drinks juices and she lives the Gerson way of life. She travels round the world, and she's how somebody of her age should be – not old and bent, but full of life and vitality. When people got very, very sick she saw that as the result of months of orthodox treatment. If only people had the faith to have her father's therapy at the beginning – or even *before* their bodies got sick.

One of the questions that frequently came up was about the therapy being low in protein. Charlotte would say, 'Protein,

protein, protein – why do people keep going on about protein? It's all this protein that clogs up our bodies and we can't get rid of it. The body doesn't know what to do with it. Too much protein causes tumours to grow. Whereas protein starvation turns *on* the immune system.

'We are having protein shoved down our throats morning, noon and night. Look at me! Here am I, in my seventies, travelling around the world, doing all these things and the only protein I ever eat is a little de-fatted cottage cheese! No meat or fish. Do you see me getting tired or lacking in energy?' She's a big Germanic woman, nearly six feet tall, and the epitome of good old age. 'We are not *meant* to die in the way that people are dying now – in pain, crying out, in fear. That's not how human beings are supposed to die. We are supposed to grow old, we go to bed one night and we don't wake up. That's how we're meant to die!'

If a chemical enters the body and doesn't meet the necessary vitamin or mineral to transform it into something less toxic, so that the body can get rid of it, it turns it into something *more* toxic. For instance, zinc and magnesium are two of the minerals that are crucial for detoxification. When I was first diagnosed, I had some nutritional tests done which showed that I was deficient in these two minerals. If something toxic goes into the body, the body needs zinc to convert it into something less toxic. If all the reserves of zinc in the body have been depleted because of your diet, the body will transform it into chloral hydrate: knock-out drops, Mickey Finns. This is why people often feel muzzy and spaced out when they breathe or eat something toxic.

It was really exciting when she spoke, she really touched something in me. I knew what she was saying was right. It was so real. Gerson was a genius. He had the courage to step outside the limitations of his own profession and he died a very unhappy man, ostracized by his peers. He had the courage to say, 'No, this isn't the right way.' All geniuses through the ages have been ridiculed and I am sure that one day the world will accept that he was one.

22

There was a young Australian there, Josh, who was a real laugh. He was only in his twenties and he had testicular cancer. It had grown upwards and a huge tumour, the size of a grapefruit, had developed in his gut. When he arrived, it was so big he couldn't bend over. He was full of life and was a great joker. He would have us in hoots of laughter. They are much more open to alternative therapies in Australia and he had been able to find out about Gerson quite easily. His mother was with him; she was so concerned about him. The doctor in Australia had told him that if he thought he was going to get better sitting on top of a mountain in Mexico drinking carrot juice, he was some sort of idiot. Just like us – we had been told, 'If you think carrot juice can cure cancer. . . .' But by the time he left, ten days before I did, his tumour had shrunk to a quarter of the size in just three weeks. I don't know what happened to him – that's the sad thing, people came and went, yet at the time we all became very close to each other.

There was a Canadian boy there with his mother who had breast cancer. She was pretty sick, and didn't have the energy to go on. He was trying to give her that energy. But the fact is that if you don't feel that energy inside you, nobody can give it to you. You have to find that source of energy yourself. You could see people struggling all the time.

All the rooms were built around a central courtyard, and there were chairs outside and on the balconies, so there was a feeling of community. Some of us could take our meals with other people in the dining room, but a lot of people who were too sick had to eat in their rooms, and everyone would go round and jolly those people along, and encourage them. There was a woman there with a mastectomy who had secondary cancer in her bones. She would lie in her bed by the open window so that as people passed they could lean in and talk to her. It was very sad: bone cancer is incredibly painful.

There was a Japanese doctor there who had come to learn about the therapy. Breast cancer is very rare in Japan because they don't eat much meat, preferring salted fish, but they have a lot of stomach cancers. Charlotte observed that the Germans have similar forms of cancers, and said that it was because of the high salt content of their diets. The Germans eat sausages which are high in nitrites and sodium, and both the Germans and the Japanese eat a lot of smoked foods. He had a young doctor with him, also Japanese, and they were living on the Gerson food while they were staying there.

One day the younger one said, 'I'm going to San Diego and I'm going to have a McDonald's!'

We looked at him very disapprovingly. The next day when he came in for breakfast he said he felt quite ill – his body had become used to all this clean food and suddenly he had put junk food into it; it had reacted in a very violent way, telling him in no uncertain terms that it didn't like it. So we all laughed and said, 'Go and have an enema and you'll feel better when you've got rid of it all!'

There was a feeling of togetherness, of having a common cause, in contrast to the feeling at home where people are frightened to mention the word cancer. Even doctors can't bear to say the word cancer. But 'cancer' is just a word, not a death sentence. Yet we see it as that. If we can see it as just a word, then perhaps we can get it into some sort of perspective. I can remember saying to Edward when I was diagnosed that I knew how people with Aids felt.

'What do you mean?' he asked.

'Well, when you mention cancer, you can almost feel people recoiling, taking a sharp intake of breath. They step back a pace, they shrink as if to say, "If I get too close to this person, I might get it too". That's how people with Aids must feel – outcasts, like lepers.'

People expect you to waste away and die, and every time they see you, they are surprised that you are still alive. When they ask you how you are, what they are really asking is, 'Are you getting near death yet?'. We don't talk to each other about cancer. How can we, as individuals, come to terms with it if nobody can talk to us about it? That's what was so refreshing in Mexico. Everyone wanted to talk about their illness. It wasn't anything frightening. Here were doctors who, when you asked them why this had happened, told you. We had lectures telling us what happened to the body and why things react in certain ways. It was wonderful to be in that environment where people were so open and honest with each other. It was a therapy in itself.

23

The anger that I felt while I was having the treatment at St Lucy's was a bit like when I had taken on the passive role of abuse. You are lying there and being done to. There I was again, in a situation which was out of my control; I was disempowered. These emotions inside you become active again when you are ill, similar feelings of having to play the passive role, not being allowed to become involved in what is happening to your body. ('You don't have to do anything, we'll do it. We'll cut it out, burn it out, whatever.') Suddenly I was in an environment where the doctor was saying, 'It's all down to you. We can show you that the power to live or to die is yours. It's not ours; we are only the guides.' In the same way as Dr John had been the guide to healing my emotional body, here was somebody saying, 'I'm the guide to heal your physical body, but you are the one who's got to do it. It's not us; we can only teach you, but then it's up to you.'

It was frightening in a way, but it was very exciting. I was embarking on a journey, but I was in the driving seat. No one else was in charge. It was down to *me*.

I had only been there a couple of days when I got this horrendous itchy rash all up my arms, and I felt awful. I nearly fell asleep over my dinner and fell into bed at eight o'clock. I woke at twenty-past one, having missed my ten o'clock enema. I felt terrible – very fuzzy-headed and not with it at all. I woke up at six-thirty still feeling awful. I was feeling pretty bad when I told the doctor, and she said, 'Good!'

'How can this be good?'

She said, 'Your body is showing it is still alive. It hasn't given up and it's telling you something. It's having cramps and feeling awful because it is still functioning. The patients we worry about when they come here are the ones who feel nothing. When you feel bad it shows you're still alive!'

So that made me feel much better about myself. But the rash

was raging, so they gave me aloe vera jelly to put all over it. Then I got mouthfuls of ulcers, which is very common on the Gerson therapy, because of the toxins coming out. They were *so* painful. Pimples were also very common. My skin is the main eliminative organ for me. The first year or so of the therapy my hands had terrible open cracks – at the joints I could almost see the bone. Thick, glue-like white stuff would ooze out, much thicker than pus.

At one point I had mucus pouring continually out of my eyes. I had great flakes of skin coming off my scalp – the body does amazing things when it is going through the healing process. If you are not in touch with this, it can be really unnerving and quite frightening. But if you see this as negative things coming out, you begin to heal yourself.

Western medicine sees fever as a negative thing, whereas the Mexico clinic positively welcomed it. Fevers are a sign that your immune system is working ('You've got a good fever – wonderful!!'), instead of a bad symptom that has to be suppressed.

The tenth day I was there, I had a 'healing reaction'. I had flu-like symptoms, felt very ill, and was in bed for three days, tearful and depressed. The psychological side of a healing reaction is strong too. You feel that you can't go on, and you want to give up. While I was having this crisis, I woke up at three o'clock in the morning and felt heat coming from under my navel, a burning sensation which was very painful. So they put clay packs on my stomach to ease it. Something amazing was going on inside, this heat was really powerful.

Something in my gut was healing, a tumour was breaking down. I now know that the body kills cancer cells by raising its temperature. It was a sure sign that my immune system was still working.

During the first six months of the therapy at home, I had the most terrible smells coming from my body. I reeked of ammonia and a strong, really powerful smell was coming through the pores of my skin. I used to notice it particularly when I took my enema. When Edward came to bed at night he used to say that when he opened the bedroom door it overwhelmed him. He said later it was so awful in bed he could hardly bear to sleep with me. It was an unbelievably strong smell. Constantly, for six to eight months, these terrible toxic gases emerged from my body. It was a joke with the children who would cry, 'Goodness, Mummy!' and I would say, 'I can't help it! It's coming from my body, there's nothing I can do.'

Although my diet wasn't perfect, it wasn't too bad, and I didn't smoke. But I was starting to drink too much just before my diagnosis, as a prop because things were beginning to disintegrate for me: I couldn't cope with life and at half-past five I would be pouring myself a drink. I thought I needed it, I thought I couldn't get through life without one. Yet now I haven't had a drink for four years and it doesn't bother me in the slightest. It just shows the power of the mind. It was only an illusion that I needed that drink to cope with life. I don't.

Personally I believe that an enormous amount of these toxins come from our thoughts, not just things we put into our bodies. For instance, if you're continually living in a state of fear, the involuntary chemical processes of the body over which we have no control, and which are happening all the time, will have an effect. When I was young, I suffered continually from stomach problems. I had a spastic colon and was always having what you might call a nervous tummy. All these chemicals were being poured into the gut all the time because I was living on the edge. I know that some people in the clinic were so toxic that the staff had to scrub the walls of their rooms after they had gone because they were black, because there was so much muck coming out of the patients' bodies.

24

I met two other patients from Britain while I was in Mexico: Bridget, a young woman in her late twenties who had melanoma, and Anna who had breast cancer. We were like the Three Mus-keteers, we were all so full of hope. When Bridget died, only a few months after we came back, it was a real blow. Anna died two years later and that was an awful shock. I am sure now that it was because they had things in their lives that they couldn't face: it wasn't so much the illness. Bridget was gay, and her parents, her mother particularly, couldn't come to terms with it. Her brother was a doctor and fitted the mould of a very middle-class family, whereas Bridget didn't fit the mould.

She was out in Mexico with her partner Beatrice who was very supportive, but when they came back to England Beatrice had to go back to work and couldn't look after her, so Bridget had to go and live with her parents. She quite often used to ring me and say, 'Oh God, I can't stand this. I've got to stay here because I need someone to help me with the therapy,' but there was this awful conflict. I met her mother once and found her overpowering. She obviously found it very difficult to come to terms with Bridget's sexuality. Bridget didn't have a chance to root out the causes of her illness, to dig the deep ground, so the therapy couldn't work.

There was a conflict between her sexuality and the way her parents viewed her. Her problem was that there was this conflict going on inside her, while all her energy was needed to combat her cancer. In the same way my energy had been used to repress both my feelings and my memory. I felt this enormous surge after the conflict had gone. The amount of energy needed to keep these conflicts in check is so great that your body hasn't got a chance to heal. It's having to use its energies on something else all the time. The immune system becomes weakened and you become susceptible to disease.

Anna and I became quite close. With her, there was a conflict with her mother. Her father was killed in the war when she was a small baby and her mother had remarried. Anna hated her stepfather and felt guilty about it. She also felt that her mother always favoured her stepfather over her. Like Bridget, Anna had unfinished business, unresolved conflicts.

Anna was Austrian and married to an Englishman, Ray. She was in the clinic on her own for two weeks. She'd had a mastectomy and deep radiation, but when they had wanted to give her chemotherapy she decided that she wasn't going to have it and had opted for Gerson instead. When we got back from Mexico we often talked on the phone and we saw each other regularly. It was a terrible shock when she died. Bridget died in October the year she came back so she didn't live that long. But Anna lived for eighteen months, and looked so well, that it was a real blow when she died.

Anna tried to be very positive, but there was a tremendous amount of fear there. Her fear showed in the way she was always doing extra things outside the therapy. She was always ringing me up and saying that she'd found a new doctor or she was going to have same different injections. She went to a man who worked with electrical energies in the body, and who used crystal therapy.

She also went to a doctor who was involved in collagen and laser therapy.

Anna had had intensive radiotherapy after her mastectomy – far more, she found out later, than had been necessary, and her chest wall was damaged. When the cancer returned it came back on the mastectomy scar. She started getting pimples along it, and when they did a needle biopsy they found that they were malignant. When she began the Gerson therapy, her scar started to ooze constantly. The doctors in Mexico saw this as poisons coming out of her system, but Anna saw it as something very bad. She was obsessed with this lesion on her chest wall that wept pus all the time. She felt angry that it hadn't happened until she started the Gerson therapy: she didn't see it as something bad coming out of her body, but as something that had to be got rid of. She ultimately went for laser treatment, and at the beginning of the summer of 1993 she told me she was going to Austria.

She was at that time feeling very well, and was going to her mother's house in Austria with Ray. She was away all summer. I phoned in mid-September and Ray said that she wasn't very well and she couldn't speak to me. The next thing I heard, a week later, was a phone call to say she had died. I was amazed. I had seen her just before she went to Austria and she looked so full of health and vitality that I could not believe it.

They had gone to Austria, first to Vienna where it had been almost unbearably hot, and from there up into the mountains where it was very, very cold. She had caught a chill which gradually got worse and worse, perhaps because of the conflicts with her mother. I didn't know this at the time, but her mother had persuaded her to come off the therapy. There was still this conflict between her and her stepfather over her mother's affections, even though he had died just before she went out. Some therapists believe that breast cancer is often about conflicts with the mother. Ray told me that the chest infection had turned into pneumonia, and it reached the stage where she was so ill that they couldn't fly back and they had to return by train. They arrived back home in London but her breathing was very bad, and the doctors said that her lungs were full of fluid. They admitted her into hospital in the end, and she had been in there a couple of days when they started to drain the fluid off the lung. Ray went in to see her one afternoon and they sat chatting, and she seemed fine. Now that the fluid was starting to go, she was looking much better. Then she said she felt a bit tired and wanted a nap, so he said he'd have a walk around and a cup of tea. When he came back, she was dead. She died in her sleep.

It was a great shock for him – she had survived all this time, and she really did look so well. He had only just spoken to her and she was gone.

Not long before she went to Austria, Anna told me that she had been to a medium. This was all part of her constant searching for something. She was always going to somebody else, and she didn't have the faith in herself that what she was doing was right. This medium had made contact with a friend of Anna's who had died of cancer the year before who said, 'We are waiting for you. It's lovely here. It's very nice, and we have a place for you.' Anna was a religious person and had often gone to church with this girl. I wondered whether she told herself then that she wanted to go. I don't know.

Yet at the beginning of the therapy she so desperately wanted to live. It's the unconscious negative conflicts coming up that always override conscious desires. It was a real blow when Anna died, a huge shock. We had been through so much together. I started to worry that if somebody looking so well could go like that, what did that say for me, although I drew comfort from the fact that Anna had had a lot of conflicts that hadn't been addressed.

In a way it's like being in a tunnel, with a light at the end of it, and you know that that is why you have got to keep digging into yourself, because otherwise you are not going to get to that light. There's always another push to make. You must not block out these things, no matter how painful; you mustn't. Anna's death disheartened me. I missed her: we'd shared so much and gone through so many things together and rung each other up when we'd had blood tests and so on. It was difficult. But it also gave me another little push in the right direction: luckily for me it didn't work in an entirely negative way.

25

Life went on in the clinic with people coming and going. I met an American lady in her mid-thirties called Harriet who was lovely.

She had a sarcoma in the soft tissues of her arm. She'd had lots of operations, including a huge lump cut out of her back, and then another at the top of her arm because it kept spreading. What had brought her to Mexico was that her doctor had wanted to remove her arm.

'They keep cutting more and more off my arm. What's it going to be next – my other arm?' She was very refreshing.

Eve, the woman who was desperately ill with breast cancer that had spread to her bones, had her husband Ian with her. When I first met Ian I thought he was very nice, but there was something I was uneasy about. He was very tactile in a way that was not quite right. Harriet told me that Ian had gone into her room and closed the door and offered to 'show her his scar'. Harriet, in typical American fashion, told him where to go. There was his wife dying of some dreadful disease. Was that *her* conflict? Had this been her problem in her life – her husband's infidelities? I felt that she knew: when Ian put his arm around me to say 'Come in dear', she'd look at him as if to say, 'Even while I'm in here like this you'll behave like this'.

It was a life of juices, food and enemas, but those of us who were well enough would go and talk to other people. In the evenings Anna, Bridget, Beatrice and I would sit and drink herbal teas out on the terrace in the lovely Mexican night. Sometimes other people would join us. Harriet's husband Bud, a real Westerner in cowboy boots, used to play his guitar to us.

An American man from Carmel who had Parkinson's disease was slowly losing the feeling in his body and he trembled all the time. His wife Olga was the most overpowering woman, so domineering that everybody bristled when she came near. It turned out that she and her husband didn't live together. They had two adult children, but after about 20 years of marriage he told her he was gay and he went off to live with his lover in San Francisco. Because he was ill, she had come to look after him. Some of us were a little cruel and said that with a wife like Olga it was no wonder that he was gay, which wasn't very nice of us. There had been a lot of bitterness from his children when they found out what was going on. We all sat out on the terrace chatting about it until it was time for our 10pm enemas. We would laugh at the dinner table or breakfast because talk was always about our lower regions! How was your enema today? It had its funny side.

One day some of the girls were going into the local town and asked if I'd like to go along. I decided that I had to conserve all my extra energy for healing so I lazed around instead. Charlotte was emphatic that we didn't use up precious energy with exercise. It was important that any energy our body was getting should be used to heal it. There were mini trampolines out in the courtyard and we were told we could use them to bounce gently because they are very good for stimulating the lymphatic system. It can become very sluggish, and rebounding is a good way of keeping it moving.

Edward used to come down to the clinic, and one time he stayed overnight. He brought the children down to see me as well. They had been snow skiing above Palm Springs, and were going to Universal Studios, so they were very excited. We spoke to each other on the telephone quite often. People who were trying to talk to their loved ones in England found it really frustrating because the Mexican phone service isn't that good. With my family just across the border, it was much easier. Knowing that they were not far away took a lot of the pressure off me.

I had the results of my blood and urine tests, and my cholesterol, much to my amazement as I was certainly not overweight, was sky high. It was 248, and the normal rate is from 132 to 200. I was amazed at this, but the doctor told me that it was most probably my liver reacting and the level should go down in a day or two. My body was not absorbing things properly, it couldn't metabolize the cholesterol which remained in the bloodstream.

It was sad to see people come and go, wondering what was going to happen to them. Then new inmates would arrive. There were two Germans one day, one a patient and the other a helper. The patient was really thin and yellow, and she was *so* disappointed. She had expected this wonderful hospital and she continually complained about how awful the place was. She was very negative. There was another American man there who had a brain tumour and he was full of gloom and doom and negativity too. Nothing was going to work. I found out that his son, a doctor, had told him that it was a waste of time and money coming to the hospital. I was sure he wasn't going to make it.

The day that Josh left there were tears from everyone. He was the life and soul of the party and it was going to be very quiet without him. Everyone was feeling very down at dinner that evening. Then Bridget and Beatrice left and we all went out to wave goodbye. Harriet felt very emotional so I tried to cheer her up. I would often pop in to her room for a cup of tea and a chat. I really liked her, and it was awful when she left a few days later. The place seemed to empty all of a sudden and all I could do was hope for some cheerful replacements!

26

I spent three weeks in the clinic learning about the therapy. When I left, I felt much more optimistic than when I arrived. Everyone was so inspiring, as was the amazing contrast between the awfulness of the hospital at home and this wonderful place. I left feeling very excited and positive.

On the day that I left they gave me flasks of juice and some jacket potatoes wrapped up in foil and a box of salad. I was warned emphatically not to touch the airline food because, having spent three months detoxifying, the salt in it would send my body into shock. It was better to eat nothing than to eat airline food.

Edward picked me up and we drove back along the Pacific Highway. We were to fly from LA to Miami to London after spending the night in the airport hotel; I was therefore going to have to go for a long time without proper food. We arrived at LA early in the evening. It was wonderful to see everybody again. I looked pretty ghastly, in fact quite yellow. My liver was in trouble; plus I had taken lots of carotene; plus I was detoxifying – which was why I was a strange colour. There were wonderful hugs all round. We then went for a meal because everyone was hungry, and I had to watch them eating!

I had a flask of coffee and tried to do an enema on the floor of the hotel suite. It was a tiny little bathroom with a cold ceramic tile floor. It was horrible. From having felt very positive, I was feeling more and more dejected. I had eaten all my food and was starting to feel a bit down.

We flew to Miami and had to wait for a connecting flight to London. By the time we arrived home I was looking, and feeling, totally desperate. Lots of people had warned me that the flight home, after all those weeks detoxifying, would be quite difficult.

You can't keep drinking juices because you then need to take the enemas. I do know someone who took an enema in an aircraft, but I didn't feel that I could, wedged against the door in those tiny spaces!

We arrived back and a friend was waiting to meet us. I was feeling terrible when we got home but luckily my juicer had arrived from the States. Somebody had bought my vegetables in, plus a supply of organic fruit. The first thing I needed was a juice, so we got the juicer going. Then I had an enema and I began to feel more human.

But that first month home was a complete nightmare. Looking back, I don't know how I coped. I had spent three weeks lying there in Mexico with somebody bringing me a juice every hour and being served meals, and suddenly I'd got to do all that myself, and cope with everything else. It was a terrible shock to the system. Someone came in three mornings a week to help, and Edward used to help at weekends with the juices, but during the week it was one thing after another. I'd have a juice and wash up the machine, then twenty minutes later it was time to do the next one. In between I was scrubbing carrots and washing lettuces and taking enemas. After thirteen juices, one every hour during the day, plus five enemas, by the end of the day I used to fall asleep at ten o'clock while doing the last enema. Plus I was ill as well, sometimes feeling worse than others.

Finding the best way to take the coffee enema proved problematic. I would attempt to stand it on the loo seat and lie on the floor, then the little tube would come off and the coffee would go all over the place. Those first couple of months were pretty tough. If I could only survive those . . .

But I threw myself into learning how to do the therapy for myself. 'I've got to do it,' I told myself. If I wanted to get better, *I* had to do it. People could help, but ultimately it was all down to me. It was enormously satisfying in one way, knowing that it was totally in my hands, and frightening in another in that it was my own responsibility.

After about six months I was desperate to go out somewhere because all that time I had remained at home. Edward took me to Milton Keynes shopping, but after only about an hour and a half I felt ill, and by the time I got back I could hardly walk and I was deathly white. It brought it home to me how fragile I was, how close to the edge my body really was. So after that I tended not to wander too far – I stayed near the safety of the juicer and the bathroom!

Lying there taking enemas for 20 minutes, which at the beginning seemed horrifying, now gave me time to think. It's incredible how quickly you learn to hold the liquid until you know it's ready to go and carry out everything with it. It was unbelievable to think of what was coming from inside *me*, all this accumulation of stuff in my body. Compared to most people, I think I had a relatively healthy diet; I didn't eat junk food, I ate lots of fruit and vegetables, I didn't eat an excessive amount of meat, although I did have a terrible weakness for cheese and I consumed large quantities of it without realizing that it contained vast quantities of salt. I had thought nothing of sitting down at lunch and eating half a pound of cheddar cheese with bread. When I think back, I also had a craving for salty foods like olives and peanuts.

I was going through a process. Because the issue is very much about you and your body and you are so involved with it, it is inevitable that you go through the mental process of looking at yourself. It's as if my body, in the act of getting rid of something, was communicating to my mind. Lots of other patients have said this to me too.

27

Nowadays I eat lentils and rice, but no pulses because they contain an enzyme-inhibitor, and no sprouted seeds for the same reason. Not many grains, but potatoes are wonderful, as is the carrot! The carrot is the only vegetable that contains all but one of the essential amino acids. It is *the* most wonderful vegetable. I eat no cakes, no sugary things, just unrefined molasses sugar, but they don't advocate that in any quantity. We have a bread made from millet and a sour-dough rye bread. The only oil we are allowed is cold-pressed flax seed oil which is very expensive.

The bulk of my food now is raw. Some people get bored with the diet and find it monotonous, but only because they are afraid of experimenting with vegetables. We tend to associate vegetables with the traditional 'meat and two veg' but there are wonderful things you can do with them. I have often sat down to eat just a jacket potato with red cabbage and apple and people say that it looks nice! The only problem with having to eat organically is that the food available is dependent upon the time of the year. It also makes eating out difficult, because even if I just have salad, it is unlikely to be organic. Occasionally I do eat non-organic food – I may see a mango when I am shopping and I buy it because I have a real taste for it.

When I was on the therapy I was eating 50lb of vegetables per week which included 30lb of carrots, 24 lettuces, 3–4lb of onions. Of course, a lot of it was in juice form, but everything had to be organic. In the States they spray apples particularly badly, and they plant their potatoes with a cup of chemicals for each one. Then they are sprayed while they are growing. When they are harvested they are sprayed again to stop them sprouting.

What happens to the plant happens to humans. The plant's immune system is damaged by the over-use of chemicals, so it can't fight off disease and it gets covered with insects. The more we use chemicals to spray plants, the more we deplete their immune system. Plus we deplete their supply of zinc and magnesium – the minerals I was deficient in, as are many cancer patients.

So what is happening to the plant is happening to us. If the soil is depleted, the plants are depleted and we are depleted. There is a worldwide increase in cancer and this kind of farming has been going on for the same amount of time as that increase. It's an obvious link. I am just the ordinary person in the street: if I can see the connection, why can't the powers-that-be see it? Gerson noticed that after the Second World War his therapy started to become much less successful. He linked it directly to the use of DDT which was banned eventually when scientists found out all the problems it was causing.

Not only over the past 20 to 30 years have we been eating more and more deficient plants, but we have also been subjected to more and more toxicity from outside. Our water and our air are polluted and so our bodies need more of the vital minerals, not less. But there are big, powerful lobbies involved and too much money is at stake for them to admit the connection. If we change this, all the chemicals that are put into the soil will go, many people who are sick will no longer need drugs and there will be less illness, so the chemical and drug industries will lose their fat profits. The vested interest is too big. Farmers say that they need the yields to feed the people, but there are huge surpluses everywhere. Third World countries are made to grow cash crops in order to pay off their debts so they are stopped from growing their food in the traditional organic way. America actually exports to the Third World chemicals which are banned in the USA.

All of this is hidden from the majority of people – they have no idea when they pick apples off the supermarket shelf what they are putting into their bodies. There should be government health warnings on non-organic produce saying, 'Eating these may damage your health. They could give you cancer'.

Organic fruit and vegetables are often misshapen and may not look as attractive as the highly polished, uniform vegetables on the supermarket shelf. But looking nice doesn't mean that they *are* nice or that they *taste* nice. People say they can't afford organic food, but you see their trolleys laden with expensive junk food as glamorized by the TV advertisements. I don't know how they can call it food. Food should be something that nourishes, but junk food is empty. Meat is full of antibiotics and hormones. BSE is the classic example of what I am saying: we have destroyed the cow's immune system, so should we be surprised that it does the same for us if we eat it?

The prevalent attitude is to get better once we are ill rather than to avoid getting ill in the first place. I have noticed that I eat far less than I used to, because the food I am getting is nourishing my body. I don't have that constant urge to eat all the time. I have a good and constant source of energy from my food. Yet there is no harm in treating yourself to a cream cake from time to time because the body is strong enough to deal with it. The real problem is what you put into your body most of the time.

The trouble is that the powers-that-be know that once they go down the path of making these connections, they are going to have to turn everything on its head, it's going to pull the rug out from under their own feet. They are too committed to the scientific and commercial way of thinking. Power lobbies are involved. There is a great investment there, a huge vested interest which doesn't want to hear this message.

As Charlotte Gerson told us in her lectures, this is exactly what happened in the States. As soon as it was seen that some of these alternatives were having some success, the power lobbies immediately reacted and a law was passed against them. In short, they were saying that people cannot take responsibility for how they are treated.

The American Constitution is all about freedom and human rights. And because it is federal, the states pass their own laws. California has actually passed a state law saying that cancer cannot be treated other than by chemicals, radiation or surgery. That is why all the alternative therapies are over the border. Radio Free America, a pirate station, is the only way people in the States can find out about alternative therapies.

There was I having to go into Mexico because 'the greatest democracy on earth' won't allow people to decide how they should be treated. How terrible that it should be like that.

28

The issue of why we haven't found a cure for cancer is complicated. So much money has gone into cancer research over the past few years, but vast amounts of it come from the drugs companies. As a result, all the so-called cures are biased towards drugs because of a vested interest.

One of the reasons that they haven't found a cure is that cancer is such a complex disease. They say they are making great break-throughs in the genetic field, yet they don't look at the emotional legacies that we pass on through families – the combination of mental, environmental, emotional and spiritual factors. Other diseases of the auto-immune system, like arthritis and diabetes and Parkinson's, also need to be considered in the same way. But people don't seem ready to hear this: they still have to be weaned off their old ideas, the safety of their familiar concepts.

Governments pump out information about how eating a particular food will help you avoid heart disease and that eating in a certain way will protect you from disease, but the food companies continue to manufacture the same old foodstuffs. What nobody will acknowledge at present is that, while food can be preventive, as for food being able to cure you when you have got the disease, that is a non-starter according to them.

Yet there are large numbers of Gerson patients in the States who are long-term recovered.

Charlotte cannot understand why the establishment is so afraid of the alternative treatments. It is a surprising fact that if you put one hundred people with terminal cancer in a room and offered them an alternative treatment which was the only likely means of survival, once they knew what it entailed only twenty-five per cent of them would choose it. Not everybody is ready: I used to spend a lot of my time and energy trying to explain to people about the Gerson therapy, but they couldn't see it. I used to get so frustrated, but now I see that 'the readiness is all'. A guide is always there for us, but whether we choose to listen is up to us. Inflicting one's convictions is a form of fascism. Everyone has their own journey.

I met a woman with melanoma – and everyone knows that Gerson is particularly successful with melanoma. She really didn't want to have the therapy, but her husband persuaded her. That was a waste of time to start with – it has to come from *you*. He was trying to make the journey for her. She came to the clinic and before returning home said to me, 'If I go on the therapy, I won't be able to play my golf.'

I felt like saying to her that she wouldn't be able to play golf *at all* when she was dead! I didn't of course.

This woman used to complain that she hated the food and that she couldn't be bothered to take the juices. It was no surprise when her husband rang a few weeks after she returned from Mexico to say that she had died. She didn't want to live and she didn't believe the therapy could make her better: if she had believed in it, it would have motivated her.

You would be amazed at the number of people who come up with every reason under the sun why they can't do the therapy. What they are really saying is that they don't think they are worth saving. This is the complexity of the disease. *Why* are they saying that? There are so many bits to the puzzle, of which psychological cleaning is one important element. There is no one *cure*. You have to do it yourself.

If you have the emotional strength, you will succeed, otherwise you will always find a reason to give up. The physical cleansing is easy once you have done the psychological cleansing. It's easiest to do it that way round, because otherwise you will always find a reason not to do the physical work every time you hit a psycho-logical problem. With Dr John I started to cleanse myself of my history, my family, my emotional past and that's the key to why I am alive now.

PART 3

Pandora's Box

We may have the experience but miss the meaning.

T S ELIOT

29

I opened a Pandora's box when I started to look into my past. Most of my original perceptions of my childhood were totally wrong. There are things that I've only recently found out, since I've been ill, which have changed my entire view of my early life. Four or five years ago, if someone had asked in general terms what sort of a childhood did I have, I would have said a reasonably happy one. But now I realize that it wasn't like that at all. I had put this rosy hue on to it. It is difficult to accept, because I feel I am betraying my family and parents by telling it like it was. There is a bit of me, even now, that is saying 'how can you be so treacherous?' It's part of the collusion that goes on in families, the collusion to keep up an image. The myth of the family.

Both my parents had been married before. My father had six children from his previous marriage and my mother had a son, who lived with his father. We never saw him and my mother never talked about him. I thought that was odd because he was as much my brother as the others were. I have only found out in the last few years that my mother's first husband was violent towards her.

My father lived in Newcastle and was in the Merchant Navy. His first wife, who was a friend of my mother's, died from septicaemia. She used to like gardening and they think she may have scratched a spot on her face with some soil on her hands and she got an infection which turned into lockjaw. At that time antibiotics were not generally available and she died quite rapidly, leaving my father with six children: four boys and two girls ranging in age from two to twelve. He could not cope without her, so he put them into children's homes – the boys went to one, the girls to another.

Their mother died when her eldest child, Harry, was twelve. He was nineteen when I was born. He never went into the children's home, because he was old enough to go into the Boys Army. Later he was always excluded by the others; he was the odd one out. Tim, Jake and Daniel would never invite him into their coterie because he hadn't gone into the home. They resented the fact that he hadn't had to go – but it was only because he happened to be the eldest.

The three other boys were sent to a home somewhere in Kent, and life was pretty tough for them. None of them like talking about it; they don't want to remember it or look at it. They received punishments like being put into cold baths, and certainly no warmth and love. I can remember my youngest sister, Muriel, who had only been two when she was put into care, saying to Jake, the brother who abused me, something about the home, and he shouted at her, 'Don't talk about it. I don't want to speak about it. Don't ever mention it to me!' Obviously she touched on something that was very painful. It is certainly possible that he himself was abused – it's how you learn these patterns. It is well known that it does happen in children's homes.

My father left his five children in the homes until they could go to work. As they became old enough, he got them each a job and brought them out. I was astonished when I found out. I couldn't believe that he could treat them like that. He must have been a Jekyll and Hyde. Whilst he was a weak man, as I saw him, the man who cared only about drinking, there had been a side to him which I never really saw: how could you do that to your own children? It's frightening. And yet they never showed any anger towards him, all the time I was growing up, so it must have been deeply suppressed. They showed anger towards each other, but they didn't direct it at the one person to whom it should have been directed. Maybe they were also angry at their mother for dying: as a child you feel anger if you think that someone has deserted you, especially if life after that becomes very difficult. 'How could you do this to me?'

My father was a small red-haired man, just over five foot tall. I remember him as very emotional, which I found embarrassing. He was a great one for crying if things upset him, putting his arms around us, and I found that difficult to cope with in a man. He was incontinent with his feelings, although not so much with anger, which he didn't display that often, unless he was pushed. I don't remember him ever hitting me, although I can remember a terrible display of anger when he and my mother were arguing. There was this photo of me aged about three, looking like a little angel, in a frame on the sideboard. He picked it up and flung it across the room and it smashed into pieces. 'She's mine and don't you forget it', he yelled at her. The argument was obviously about me. But on the whole, although there was a lot of anger in the family, it didn't come from him. There was just this awful mushy emotion all the time. Yet he was very loving to me as a child.

He had a drink problem, which was always denied by everyone in the family. When I was growing up I found his drinking very embarrassing. I was always told to leave him alone and that he was all right. I can remember him drinking at seven in the morning. He would get emotional and stupid and weepy and that irritated me intensely. He was never able to take responsibility, and he was hopeless with money. My mother had to do everything. He had four sons who were all nearly six foot tall, and yet this small man seemed to wield enormous power over them. Not only did my father not take them out of the homes until they were able to work, but when he did, he then took all the money they earned and gave them back a small amount of pocket money. That money was keeping me and my mother! No wonder there was enormous resentment towards me. I still find it hard to believe. My memories of him are of a weak and pathetic man, but the fact is that he had this power over them. When I found him drinking, they would tell me to leave him alone – it's as if they had to protect him in some way.

My father died just after I got married in 1976. I heard him crying all through our wedding service. I was so embarrassed. He had some breathing difficulties during the long hot dry summer and it was June when they took him into hospital. I wanted to see him but my mother said not to and, that he was all right. The next day I got a phone call at six in the morning saying he had died in hospital during the night. I suppressed it for a long time, but recently I suddenly had all this anger towards my mother coming up because she denied me seeing him before he died. But it had been a terrible shock to her – she didn't know he was going to die, and she couldn't believe it herself. But she was always trying to protect me – 'I'll cope, darling. You mustn't see anything that might upset you.'

The post mortem showed that he was riddled with cancer. It was everywhere. It had started with bowel trouble some years back and ended up in his lungs. When he died, my eldest brother Harry wept and sobbed at the funeral service – he was completely distraught.

30

Father was very weak and ineffectual, but my mother protected me and was the glue that kept the family together. She was my saving grace, but she was very secretive and kept things from me. She is now in the early stages of dementia, so about eighteen months ago I went up to her flat and took away a tin box with some of her papers in it in case anything happened to her. In it I found their marriage certificate. They didn't get married until I was eleven, and I never knew! What actually happened was that my father *hadn't* married my mother; he'd had an affair with her while she was married to her first husband and he was a widower, and I was conceived. The fact that they hadn't told me upset me terribly: I must have gone off to school that day and they went out and got married. Everyone else knew but me. I was so angry.

It made me wonder what else I hadn't been told the truth about. It was difficult for me to realize that things weren't as they appeared. From what I gathered, her previous husband would not divorce her, so when he died my parents were able to get married. I still feel that there are things that I have not been told by the family, but that is part of their pattern.

My early years were not a happy time for a small child, but my mother was always there to protect me. She was the thing that held my life together. She did everything for my father, and waited on him hand and foot, which as I got older made me more and more angry. She faced a lot of antagonism from the others. My father would sit in his chair and all you could hear was 'Lucy! Get me this! Lucy! Get me that'. Sometimes she would even come down from upstairs to fetch something for him and it would infuriate me. He was the 'poor me' type. He had been an only child, and his mother was an alcoholic. Patterns.

Having had an enormously close bond with my mother all my life, I went through a lot of anger towards her when I remembered my abuse. Why did she allow that to happen? Did she know about it? All these awful thoughts came into my mind. I have to believe that she didn't know, otherwise it would shatter all my other beliefs about her. She has been the rock in my life. She's been stable, warm and loving, but part of me wanted to shake her and ask her why she allowed my father to manipulate her as he did. But knowing him, and now hearing what others thought about him, he was obviously a very manipulative type of man. Everyone felt sorry for him – why, I don't know – but the 'poor me' is very powerful for some women, as it gives them a role. My mother had looked after her father too – she had always played the maternal role, the unselfish martyr.

The first memories I have are of leaving Newcastle to live in London when I was about three. We were all together, except for my eldest brother who by then had married, and was still in the army. The rest of us – three boys, two girls and myself – moved down to London in about 1947 because there were no jobs in the North East. We all, except for two of my brothers, lived in a flat, which was a dreadful place. I have strange memories of living there and I do wonder if there were other traumas going on there which I have repressed, which I can't or don't want to bring to the surface. I know that it was terribly cramped – me, my two sisters, Victoria and Muriel, my parents and Tim, my second brother who worked at night. We girls used to sleep together and Tim would come home in the morning and have our room to sleep in during the day. My parents had the other room.

I can remember another little girl, the same age as me, whose mother died of cancer. I remember that having a terrible effect on me. Her name was Elaine. I have strange dreams about those times, dreams that I don't fully understand. I know there are things from that time that I don't remember.

One of the nice things I can remember is coming home from school when I was 10 or 11. My mother would always be cooking something, the fire would be lit and there would be a thick slice of bread and jam and a mug of chocolate. But on the whole everyone had their own little dramas going on and there was no close connection between any of the children. I passed my 11-plus examination and went off to grammar school which caused a lot of resentment. ('We didn't have your opportunities and we couldn't have done those things.')

I had to travel quite a distance to school, where I met a girl with whom I became very good friends. She had a very unhappy relationship with her mother and we were drawn to each other. She often used to stay at our house because she felt it was warm and loving and lacked the things that she had at home. If you met her mother, you'd understand what I mean. Despite all the things that were going on in my family, my mother was a very loving and giving person. She took Anita into the bosom of the family and would bake cookies for her. I can remember going back to Anita's house and her mother who was incredibly house-proud, was standing there looking at me as if I were some piece of slime. We would walk into the kitchen and she wouldn't say anything.

Anita was a rebel and was constantly getting into awful trouble. I was this timid little girl who wouldn't say boo to a goose, yet here I was, best friends with this outrageous girl who spent most of her life outside the headmistress's room for the things she had done. We were kept separated in class. She became pregnant when she was sixteen. She was a classic case of someone looking for the love she wasn't getting. But her parents' reaction made me think that pregnancy meant being spurned by your family. It had an enormous effect on me.

There wasn't enough room for us all in the flat, so my grandmother took in two of the boys when we moved down to London. She was my mother's mother, and was still quite young because she had only been fifteen when my mother was born. She was a very tough lady, totally selfish, with three daughters of whom my mother was the eldest. My grandfather had been a coal miner before they moved to London, and he had the coal miner's disease of the lungs. All I can remember of him as a child is him staying in bed, coughing and coughing. My grandmother was always off out dancing or having fun, so my mother was the one who really looked after him.

Jake, my brother who raped me, and Daniel, my youngest brother, stayed at my grandmother's just down the road. Recently I made the horrifying discovery that Jake had been sleeping with my grandmother. They were having sex when he was about seventeen. She was no blood relation to him, but nevertheless . . . At first I could not believe it, but my brother Daniel has confirmed it. When I told him about Jake raping me he said that he wasn't surprised. He said that Jake had a basic sexual problem. He said

to me, 'You know he was having sex with grandmother? He used
to boast about it.'

So there they were, living up the road, my grandfather dying
of this disease and my grandmother sleeping with my brother.
It was grotesque. She must have been in her early fifties, he was
17. It is very hard for me to understand this, but everyone says
that it's true so I have no reason to doubt it. And from what I
know of him now, I am not surprised; and my grandmother was
a very selfish lady. The fact that her husband was dying would
not have stopped her from having her own pleasure. If he was
unable to fulfil the physical side of their marriage, which he
hadn't done for years, she then saw no reason not to look
elsewhere.

Daniel must have been only fourteen, and he was seeing his
elder brother having sex with his grandmother and boasting
about it. He told me that she used to walk around in her
underwear. There must have been so much intrigue going on. I
was only very small and not a party to it, which is why I had
these feelings of secrets going on around me. It's an awful thing
to say that that sort of thing was going on in my own family,
but it was.

I used to feel that it was *my* shame. But now I know that it is *not*
my shame; it's someone else's. It is difficult to separate things that
happen in your family, and recognize that they are *not you*. You
don't have to feel the guilt for them. But of course some people
want us to feel the guilt for them. I could never have said this a
few years ago, because I would have felt that I would be judged.
But now I have learned that I don't have to be judged on what *they*
have done. It goes back to the incest issue: one of the reasons that
we can't talk about it is that we feel we are going to be judged.

31

Then we moved to a house in the same area, but away from my
grandmother. There were now my three brothers, my two sisters
and myself. I was going to school by now. I remember all sorts of
arguments between my brothers who were always fighting. I can't
remember any happy times from then. There were four bedrooms

in the house. My two sisters and I shared one room, my parents had another, and my two brothers, Jake and Daniel, each had their own rooms. Tim got married and moved away. I grew up aware of this terrible animosity between the other two girls. Victoria, the elder, was very thin and angular. She was not a pretty girl, as she had large feet and was rather masculine-looking. Muriel, the younger one, was round and buxom with long curly hair. She was soft and feminine which was the cause of part of the antagonism. I remember violent fights between them: Victoria would attack Muriel because she would borrow her clothes. Because Muriel was bigger, she would stretch them or pull the seams and there would be terrible arguments.

There was a big age difference between the girls – when they were put into a home Muriel was only two and Victoria was ten. I found out later that my father had got a job in a shipyard for Victoria when she came out of the home! In the North East in those days it was either the shipyards or the coal mines, as there wasn't much else. Can you imagine working with all those men, having just come out of a children's home? Was it any surprise that she was the way she was?

I don't know what had happened to Victoria, but she had an incredibly sadistic streak in her. She had no imagination about fear: it wasn't that she was unafraid of anything, but if she was coming home from a dance late at night, she would walk down this dark footpath, even though it was pitch black and people had been attacked down there. Grown men wouldn't even walk down there. My mother used to worry about it, but Victoria had no imagination about what might happen. She used to frighten me intensely and used to enjoy every minute of it, probably because she was sadistically treated herself.

My mother recently told me a story which illustrated Victoria's sadism. When I was very small, they had all sat down to a meal and my mother went out of the room. When she came back in again nobody was eating. When she asked what was the matter, nobody said anything; they all just sat there with Victoria looking very smug. It turned out that she had told the others that my mother had put poison in the food! That was typical Victoria. She had an enormous capacity for lying, which was one of the things that irritated my brother Jake particularly. ('For God's sake, Victoria, you don't know truth from fantasy.') She would weave these totally amazing lies, and it was very difficult to know when she

was telling the truth. Whenever she frightened me, I would cry
and tell my mother, but she would always deny it. I was a very
frightened, nervous child because of Victoria's actions. She *loved*
to frighten me.

Victoria never had any children herself, and she didn't marry
until she was over forty. When she died from brain cancer she was
only forty-eight. Her death had a deep effect on my father: it was
a big shock to him that one of his children should die before he
did. Victoria's husband was a born flirt and I am sure he was
having affairs behind her back. They told him that she had cancer
in the brain, that it was inoperable and that they thought she had
got about three months to live. They moved her back to the local
hospital and she was left in a bed to die. He would not have her
at home. Just occasionally he would take her out for the day. I was
an adult by this time, in my twenties. They decided not to tell her
what she had got. That was terrible: she would say, 'I've got
cancer, haven't I? I'm going to die,' with this piercing look. I had
strict instructions not to tell her, so I had to sit there and deny it.
She spent those six months in torment. It would have been better
to have told her. Part of her knew anyway. When her hair grew
back after surgery, it was totally white. She gradually lost all
feeling. The terrible thing was that her body was dying, but her
brain still knew what was going on. She started to go black with
gangrene down one side. There was nothing the nurses could do.
She was just left in bed to die, with no treatment for six months.

So all these romantic images of this wonderful happy family
were total myths. Perhaps it was something I had conjured up in
my mind to repress all the things that were so awful.

32

Something happened to me in my adolescence that had a huge
impact on me. When Muriel was sixteen and I must have been
seven, I can remember hushed talking and arguments going on in
the house. I didn't know what was going on, but people were
shouting at each other. I didn't know what was happening because I was told, 'Oh, you're too young, it's nothing to do with
you'. It turned out that Muriel was pregnant. My father disowned

her. He said, 'Out you go and don't ever come back.' That's what
he did to his own daughter. He cut her off. I remember my mother
pleading with him to let her come back, but he wouldn't.

Harry and Muriel never spoke to each other for forty years after
that. Apparently my father decided to bring the police into it. He
then put all the burden on my brother's shoulders. ('You're the
eldest, you've got to deal with this.') Consequently there was
enormous antagonism between Harry and Muriel. My father
was telling him what he had to do, and the fact is that, even though
Harry must have been in his twenties, he did as he was told. Here
was this little man, whom most of them could have squashed, who
wielded this huge power. This is what I find so amazing now.
He reminds me of Napoleon, and all the other dictators who were
five foot nothing – Stalin, Hitler, Ceaucescu. What a coward not
to do it himself!

Muriel was taken in by Tim and his wife, in what was maybe a
manipulative move to get at my father. But then, horror of horrors,
the baby was black. For my father, the most died-in-the-wool
racist you can imagine, that was the ultimate sin. If he had had
any thoughts about having her back, that put the lid on it.

There were these awful feelings in the house but no one ever
explained them to me – all I knew was that Muriel had gone away,
and that my father had cut her off and wouldn't have anything to
do with her. Muriel married the baby's father. He was from
Grenada. My father was the epitome of the working-class man,
and despised 'niggers' as he called them. White people just did
not marry black people. My mother was not like that at all – she
was very open. It amazes me now, looking back and knowing
what I know now, how my mother ever came to marry my father.
People sometimes do leap into something else unsuitable when
they are trying to escape from an unhappy marriage.

When Muriel had gone there was just Victoria and me. Victoria
had a field day. Every night she would whisper, 'Someone's going
to come up the stairs to get you . . .' As a small child I was
absolutely terrified, and even at fifteen or sixteen I would not go
upstairs to bed on my own unless someone else was upstairs too.
It had an enormous and lasting effect on me. I frequently had
nightmares, really scary ones where I used to wake up screaming.

All through my life I've had enormous sexual difficulties. Part
of it was to do with the abuse but it was also connected with what
happened to Muriel. I now began to feel that sex was something

terrible: if you did it and got pregnant, you were disowned by the family and cast out. So I grew up frigid and this caused me a lot of problems in relationships. I could never give myself physically because of this terrible fear.

33

Jake was always the quiet one. He never said very much but he was a bit like a volcano; there was a lot bubbling away beneath the surface and if he got angry it came out like a huge spewing mass. But it took a lot to get him angry. He knew that his anger was dangerous. I remember him screaming to my mother, 'Keep Tim away from me or else I'll kill him.'

Jake was very quiet and secretive and never said very much about what he was doing. Daniel, the youngest brother, was the one I got on very well with. I loved him dearly. Jake and Daniel decided to emigrate to New Zealand when I was thirteen and at puberty, which obviously says something. I didn't connect it at the time, but not only did he go away, but he also took my favourite brother with him. That was difficult for me: Daniel was always happy and singing. I always felt that he loved me. Whereas the others found me a pain in the neck, he would take me to the cinema and other outings. He was a very warm person, unlike the others. I never really knew Harry, the eldest, because I never grew up with him. He felt he was outside the family, because he hadn't had our experiences of family life.

If you went up the stairs in our house, there was long corridor and the first room on the right was the room in which my sister and I slept. The first room on the left almost opposite was Jake's room. I was about eight when it happened. I had gone into his room, frightened after having a nightmare, to be comforted. But I got more than comfort. The images came back to me during that hypnotherapy session when Dr John said, 'you are walking through the meadow and there's somebody with a picnic, and he's turning around now . . .' As he turned around, the images flashed into my mind – his face, the rape.

There are big blanks after that. When Jake decided to go to New Zealand he had a girlfriend. He was very attractive, and considered quite a catch amongst the girls. The idea was that when he had got settled out there she was going to follow him. He and Daniel went by boat on an assisted passage – they were desperate for people out there in those days. The next thing we heard was that he had got married! He had met somebody on the boat and had married her because she was expecting a baby. He obviously could not do without sex. The fact that he had left somebody behind meant nothing to him. Kate, my niece who was the product of that union, told me that her mother, who is now an alcoholic, always brings this up if there are arguments. ('Well, if it hadn't been for you, I wouldn't have married him.') And yet Kate says that they need each other, and they feed off each other. He's had numerous affairs and treats her badly; she settles in one place and he plucks her up and moves her somewhere else.

Daniel told me that Jake raped his fiancée before he left, then he got on the boat and proceeded to have sex with another woman. Who knows, if he was abused in the children's home maybe it gave him an unnatural appetite for sex. People say that abuse can have one of four effects: you become extremely promiscuous; you became frigid and fearful, like me; you become gay; or you become an abuser yourself.

Jake had three daughters. He has no contact whatsoever with his children now; they won't have anything to do with him. I thought it very strange at the time when Kate went to live with Daniel and his wife. We knew nothing of what was going on, so we all thought it was most odd to abandon her own family at the age of 16.

Kate has since told her ten-year-old son not to be alone with Jake. Her sisters have had unhappy marriages and so has she. Once when her mother had left him because she found out he was having an affair, Kate went round to stay with him because he was feeling very morose and sorry for himself. She woke up one night, suddenly aware of someone in bed with her. It was her father. He was stark naked. When she shouted, 'What the hell are you doing?' he tried to put his arms around her and said, 'Your mother doesn't understand me.' Kate said, 'This is just not appropriate; you cannot do this.' She later told her mother about it but her mother's attitude was just to drink more and bury her head deeper in the sand. Kate came to England to get away from him. Thirteen thousand miles is not far enough for her.

Jake worked for General Motors as an executive. He was always the clever one, the one with the sharpest brain. Kate said he was obsessed with his children's education and with going to University. He resented the fact that he had been deprived of those things himself, so he was ambitious for his children. Considering his beginnings, he was very successful. But behind the mask, he was a sham.

Muriel told me that she can remember when she was younger dancing with him at parties. He would push himself against her and she could feel him being aroused. He obviously wasn't fussy about who he was with. I don't think that he will die of cancer: he is getting his anger out of his system in another way, by punishing other people. There may be an element of revenge in his sexuality – if Jake felt really angry with his mother for dying, perhaps he wanted to wreak vengeance on women for the rest of his life. Whereas the others seemed to have internalized their anger, he's directed his outwards through his member.

Dr John put forward the theory that if the abuse continued once I reached puberty, there was the risk that I might reveal what had happened, or that I might have become pregnant. Anyway, Jake suddenly disappeared to the other side of the world. He cut himself off from the rest of his family. He used to be quite close to Daniel, and in fact they married two sisters.

Daniel is still in New Zealand, but Jake is in Australia now. He's been quite successful out there and has a beautiful house with a swimming pool. Muriel went out a few years ago to stay with Jake. Before leaving, she bought him a crystal vase. When she gave it to him he said, 'I don't want that. It's a load of junk', and he threw it in the bin and it stayed there. He is a bastard. Daniel, who is a warm and giving person, told me that many times over the years he had lent Jake money for various things. One day Daniel needed money for a project, so he asked if Jake could lend him this money. Jake said, 'Yes, but I want five per cent interest!' Daniel said, 'You're joking, of course,' and Jake said, 'No, I'm not'. Daniel couldn't believe it.

34

The awful thing is that I grew up knowing so little about my family. Everyone was operating behind masks. I myself am still repressing things – I am sure there's a lot more hidden in my unconscious and from time to time I get bits of it coming back. After all these years I am still trying to uncover things, but nobody wants to help me. They want to keep it all hidden. It's easier for them to pass the patterns on than to challenge them, let alone change them. My mother has gone blind and I sometimes think to myself how symbolic that is – not wanting to see what is there.

I grew up with a romantic illusion, and nobody ever told me that it was wrong, that there were these poor children who had been put into homes when their mother died, but that then my mother had come along so they all came out and we all lived this beautiful happy life together. In fact it wasn't like that at all. My father did *not* bring the other children out of the homes. I have only just found out that they didn't come out of the homes when I thought. I have always felt a lot of anger directed towards me from them, and that was the reason for it.

This is the first time I have been able to talk about my father without feeling really angry. I have talked about him a lot, but now the anger is diminishing. At the beginning I had so much anger inside me that I could hardly express it. This is why it is so important that these stories are told. Once those feelings are expressed, they no longer have the same power over you; as in the visualization, the idol crumbles and you see it has got feet of clay, so you realize that it can't hurt you any more, and how powerless it is. And yet I lived in fear for all those years.

What an awful family! Harry and Daniel were the only ones who ever asked how my mother is; the others have totally cut her adrift. When Daniel came over from New Zealand, he went to see her and took her presents. Harry and his wife always sent her money at Christmas and birthdays. Jake has isolated himself from everybody now. Tim was always filled with lots of anger. When I saw him at Harry's funeral, it was quite frightening because it was just like looking at my father. I almost gasped when he walked into the room. Yet when I went to hug him, it was like hugging a board. It's a sad family; we are so apart from each other.

Now we are all cut off from each other, and there is no feeling of warmth, support or loyalty. Daniel was over here from New Zealand and he was supposed to see Harry. He went within ten miles of the door, but he didn't look him up. He sent some flowers to the funeral but hasn't spoken to Harry's wife. Harry died a few years ago, of cancer too. Yet of all of them, Daniel is probably the one most ready to look at himself; he's the gentlest and most human. When I was trying to find out things he was definitely the most forthcoming, whereas Harry's attitude, when I first told them about the abuse, was 'well, yes, I'm sure it happened, but it's a long time ago and you want to forget about it'. I never spoke directly to Tim, but I was told that he didn't believe it. There was always more anger from Tim than anyone else, and his wife fuelled his anger constantly in a very negative way. Tim had half of his lung removed some years ago, and recently died of cancer. I spoke to Muriel briefly, but although she believed me, she was a bit dismissive.

It feels like the end of a chapter. The family is a part of my life that I have got to leave behind. It has taken me four years to work through these feelings. It surprises me now that I no longer react as I used to: I have discharged them. They no longer have any power over me. Freeing myself has been a major part of my recovery, the therapeutic re-experiencing of the traumas of the past, and the letting-go, whereas my friend Yvonne couldn't do either and paid the terrible, ultimate price. She wanted the Gerson therapy to make her better, but she could never take responsibility to confront her history honestly and deal with her deepest fears.

35

I didn't actually ever meet Yvonne; our relationship was over the phone. An ex-Gerson patient who had helped me at the beginning of the therapy called me and said, 'There's somebody on the therapy who's very frightened and needs to talk. She's rung lots of people because she's so afraid.'

Even though Yvonne wanted to do the therapy, she was certain it wasn't going to work. I said I would speak to her.

Yvonne was incredibly distressed. She had been diagnosed with breast cancer that August and had had breast surgery, which she found very traumatizing. She used to say that she was proud of her breasts and they were very much a part of her. Every time she looked down, she didn't feel *whole*. She felt that it wasn't just her breast that had been cut off, it was as if a bit of her soul had gone, a part of herself that she had loved. She identified closely with her body, and said she felt that she had abused it dreadfully in her life and that now it was catching up with her. She'd been through all the hoops of bulimia and purgatives and diuretics and slimming. I remember thinking that lymphoma is one of those cancers where you can hardly see that someone's got it, and it can't be treated by cutting something out, but breast cancer is very much a visible cancer.

Some women see the removal of a breast as the bad bit being taken away and the rest of the body being whole. But for Yvonne it wasn't like that. The removal of her breast was a terrible disfigurement, something that she couldn't live with.

People told me that they found her draining. I was told to be careful, because I was healing, and should not let her take my energy. One or two people had found that, because she was filled with fear and had so much negative energy, if they didn't feel confident and couldn't trust their inner ways, they were sucked dry. Some people felt very ambivalent about speaking to her at all. You could talk to her for hours and hours and never make any progress. With someone who is so ill, you feel that you have to be compassionate, so it is difficult to be honest.

It was autumn 1991 when I started to talk with her, just before she went to Mexico. She spent five weeks out there, whereas most people only have two or three. She was consumed with fear, as if she was saying, 'I know I'm doing all these things, but it's not going to make any difference. I'm going to die anyway.' She almost said those exact words.

When Yvonne phoned, I knew I was in for a long session. She would call several people, systematically asking us all the same things, as if she had to keep looking for something but couldn't take hold of it even when it was presented to her. She had many lifelines thrown to her, but she couldn't reach out and grab them. Her own self-destruct mechanism was in place and she couldn't stop it. It was like a clock ticking away.

I can remember her saying to me, 'I knew something bad was going to happen to me. I've got this wonderful life now, and a new relationship with George' (whom she had just married, her first marriage at the age of about forty-five). 'I've finally got him, and now I'm going to lose him.' She sounded rather like a spider spinning a web around him. 'It is almost as if now, just when my life is lovely, something is striking it down,' as if she was expecting it. She was convinced that now that she had found this happiness, something would wreck it.

She would do most of the talking while I listened. Most of the talking, both before and after her trip to Mexico, was about her cancer growing bigger and overtaking her. I tried to reassure her, but in fact, as other people had found, she didn't really want to be reassured. We were being sucked dry, because no matter what we said, she always found a reason why that couldn't be. You could never convince her. She would always talk herself out of any positive thoughts, and the negative ones would completely squash them. Sometimes she would talk to me for an hour at a time and I would feel desperate. Having had my own experience of the Gerson therapy and knowing what it had done for me, I knew what was going to help her, but I could not get through to her. Part of her was struggling to grasp at something, but her unconscious fears would slap her down again every time.

She kept saying to me, 'Why aren't you afraid? Why are you like this? How can you be like this? How can you be so strong? So optimistic? I can't believe that you're not frightened.'

I said, 'No, I know I'm doing the right thing. I know I'm not going to die.'

She could not grasp that. She kept phoning me because a part of her wanted to find the answer. She wanted to be like that herself, but her fear came down like a huge blanket and pushed her wishes out of the way. Her fear was too great.

36

Then one day Yvonne said to me, 'I was abused by my father.'

It came out quite naturally, but in a very detached way, almost as if she was telling me about someone else, that it wasn't really her. It was some other girl that her father had raped. She was saying that it was herself, but she wasn't *feeling* that it was her; the incest belonged to someone else. Every time I tried to talk to her about it, she was cold and clinical. There were no feelings of anger, yet she was full of fear and cried terribly sometimes because she felt that she was going to die. But when she talked about the incest, it was as if her feelings got switched off.

'I know that I'm going to die.'

It was almost a self-fulfilling prophecy. She was convinced. Looking back and knowing what I know about her story now, it was a statement of 'I'm worthless, because of what I am.' That is how abuse makes you feel, worthless; it damages your self-esteem. It was almost as if she was saying she was worthless and what was going to happen was a logical conclusion. The guilt and the shame is very common with abused people.

Her fear was a direct result of incest. I had felt like that too. When she was talking to me I realized that this was how I was, and this was the road I would have gone down. The frightening thing was that this could so easily have been me.

I told her what had happened to me and I said, 'I was like you. I was frightened, but I went to see Dr John and finally released these suppressed feelings about my abuse. Suddenly the fear had gone and I had this strength. It was as simple as that.' I was trying to give her some of my strength by telling her what had happened. But instead of using illness, as I did, for healing her life, dealing with the past and having better relationships, it destroyed her. The reason it destroyed her was that she could not acknowledge that what was happening to her was directly related to the abuse. She wouldn't face it.

Very commonly when people are involved in incest there is terrible guilt because some of the feelings are pleasurable. It was something that I found very difficult to face up to. Incest awakens a child's sexual feelings before they are emotionally ready to cope with them. That is not to say that those feelings aren't often pleasurable. It took me a long time before I could recognize that fact. It is *the* hardest part, recognizing those feelings. It *should not* be pleasurable, so you feel enormous guilt about it.

I could see Yvonne was going downhill. I have seen this in other people too, that when their fear really overtakes them, they start looking around for alternatives. She was running around trying everything – a hydrogen peroxide treatment, a so-called life-giving fluid from America to inject into herself, NLP, some strange tablets from Germany, the lot. Faith in the therapy and belief that her body would be healed were lacking.

This is why people fail at the Gerson therapy; their fear overtakes them. It is a long, laborious, tough, frightening therapy which requires a lot of courage and will-power. You are, believe me, on your own. There's no supportive doctor here when you get back; the Gerson staff are thousands of miles away. The medical profession here are very hostile to anything like this.

There is no one to turn to, only the other people on the therapy, most of whom are going through their own healing. You need a healer figure at this time. This was what kept me going, that I had one inside me, so I wasn't frightened. But most people return home, having spent a few weeks in Mexico being closeted, having juices made for them, being surrounded by people full of hope and positive motivation. Then friends come round and you can tell by the way they look and the way they speak that they don't believe that what you are doing is right. I can remember people saying to my husband behind my back, 'I don't think Eileen should be doing this.' There is an enormous amount of negative feeling. Every time you go to your GP for a blood test you get a lecture about how you shouldn't be doing this. I never went near any of the established medical profession, as I was not going to subject myself to their negativity. The only time I did was when I had a scan in November 1993 and I felt so bad afterwards that I vowed that I would never do it again. I didn't need it.

It's the 'nocebo' effect – the opposite of placebo. If you are told something negative, it has a negative effect on the body which would not have happened had there been a positive message or no message at all. When I was first diagnosed, I remember somebody talking to me about positive thinking: they knew someone with lymphoma who had been told that they were going to die but not for about five years. You could say that was a reasonable prospect, not a bad prognosis, not an imminent death: it was well into the future, but this man died within three weeks. There was no physical reason why that should have happened. But this man said to himself, 'I cannot face the next five years going through treatment, chemotherapy and radiotherapy and the rest', so he just died. He told himself, 'I don't want to live.'

There was this conflict within Yvonne: part of her was desperately saying 'I want to live', but this unconscious thought 'you're worthless, and this is what you can expect for someone like you' is what killed her.

37

I suggested to Yvonne that she see Dr John and she said she would. He agreed to go and see her. In my naïvety I thought that once she had seen him everything would be all right, that he would show her the way out like he'd shown me.

He and I had long discussions about the question of inner strength. I would say, 'This is amazing stuff. It opens up endless possibilities if everyone can get in touch with this resource.'

He said, 'I don't agree.'

Whereas I felt that it's within everyone's capabilities, and that we've all got it inside us, he thinks that our inner strengths vary. Some people have it and others don't.

When I spoke to Yvonne after she'd seen him, things weren't any different. I was horrified. She was still full of fear, and nothing had changed. She was a bit dismissive, and said, 'Oh, he was very nice and we talked, but we didn't really achieve anything.'

Then I spoke to him: 'I appreciate you can't divulge things because of client confidentiality, but why couldn't you reach her?'

'Well, she doesn't want to be reached.'

'But she's going to die.'

'Well, we all like to punish ourselves if we are full of guilt. What do you think the ultimate punishment is? It's death.' That was all he said. 'I'm sorry but it's a futile exercise.'

I said to her, 'What did he say?'

'Oh, he wanted to talk about my father and what had happened, and I said to him, "I don't see what that's got to do with what's happening to me now".'

'It's got *everything* to do with what's happening to you now,' I said, but she could not bring herself to face this.

Knowing how I felt, and the reason why I had suppressed my feelings for all those years, I could understand what she was going through. When we love a parent or a sibling, it is unconditional love; we love them whatever. To turn round suddenly and say that they aren't loving, that they aren't these wonderful people, is the most impossible thing to do. It was difficult enough for me with my brother, but for your own father, the ultimate idealized figure, it must be so painful.

I only really started to heal when my anger started to come out. Yvonne never even felt any anger. She was so detached; all the feelings associated with her abuse were totally repressed, which is why when she spoke about it, it was as if it hadn't really happened to her.

From my own experience, it's not until you can get through to the anger that things change. It's the anger which is the destructive thing. You have to give expression to the anger, and get it out. Crying and talking about it aren't the same as reaching the thing that is damaging you. The anger is the hardest thing to get at, because when you admit that you are angry you are actually saying that this person is *bad* and realizing that the love isn't what you thought it was. That is so hard, particularly in the case of a parent.

After my hypnotherapy, I still didn't want to face what had happened, even though the memory had come up. I screamed and cried, but I still didn't want to deal with it. I would lie awake at night with my conscious mind telling me that I had simply made it all up. There were awful conflicts between what was real and what wasn't. Voices saying 'he's a wonderful person, he wouldn't do this to you. Do you realize what the implications are for the rest of your family?' all conspired to push it down again. This is another reason why I feel strongly that to stop this pattern in families, somebody has got to say 'No! this *did* happen.' It's extraordinary how, even when the rest of the family knows what has gone on, you still have to behave as if things were normal and play a part, because nobody else will condemn the abuser. You have to survive in this situation while everyone else accepts the terrible injustice. There's dishonest collusion where what you need is honest collision.

I've had that dishonest collusion from my own family: 'We accept that it most probably happened, but it was a long time ago so you must forget about it.' One member of my family even said, 'No, I don't believe that happened.' You get huge denials and perversions because people do not want to acknowledge what is happening. But having said that, it is a painful thing for them to handle. The reason why I was able to handle it when I hadn't ever looked at it before was that I had the biggest motivator of all:

death. Nothing motivates you more than that. Suddenly my sub-conscious was telling me: 'you either give this up now, or we are no more.' I believe that is why I got the cancer: without that motivation I would never have faced up to what had happened. Dr John had said to me – and I thought at the time 'what a callous man' – that we get the illnesses we need. But he was right. It was what I needed, because without the fear of what cancer was going to do with me, I would never have let those feelings out.

That's the sad thing with Yvonne, that even having been faced with that huge motivation of death, she could not let go of her secret feelings. She tried to, a little bit, but she let go of the rational part of it; she didn't let go of the feelings. Yet she had every opportunity. It was handed to her on a plate and she refused. So, as I see it, the anger caused her cancer and her fear caused it to grow.

What you acknowledge in your rational mind has got nothing to do with working it through emotionally. Psychotherapy is all on a rational, conscious level. Yvonne could have gone to therapy for years and talked about her father's abuse, but unless all those feelings start to emerge, and you re-experience them, therapy is worthless. *'You can't heal unless you feel.'* Alice Miller, the distinguished author of books on child abuse and a doctor of philosophy, said, ' "no feel, no heal" is a very apt saying.' In her experience, it was only when she could *feel* the pain of the past that things started to get better. Dr John said exactly the same thing to me: 'If you talk about anything for long enough you can rationalize it.' He did not believe in traditional psychoanalysis: 'You just keep talking around things; it's just about conscious thoughts and not allowing deep feelings to come up.' That's why people keep going to analysis for years on end, just going round and round in circles talking, but it doesn't help them with the *feelings*. The feelings have to be exorcized, not just talked about. You have to re-enter the experience.

The rational mind will generate more and more fear about crossing over the threshold into feelings. Yet once the door is opened, things are so much easier. It's one thing to talk about events in your life; it is entirely another to *feel* the pain from long ago. The rational mind will throw up more fears to help suppress those feelings. Finding the courage to open the door is the impor-tant thing – it *is* a Pandora's box! What am I going to find when I open this door? There are going to be some very nasty things that float out.

In hypnotherapy you release the feelings that go with the experience. It's a brilliant way of accessing old material immediately. In the right hands, it is the way to access those thoughts and feelings quickly, especially for cancer patients who haven't got years to spend with a psychotherapist. People are so afraid of letting go, of letting the mask slip. It *is* frightening. So you have got to do it in a very safe place – that's where hypnotherapy is preferable to other kinds of sessions because it cuts through the layers very quickly and stops the conscious mind throwing up red herrings. The conscious mind is quiet.

Let's face it, when you know that somebody has taken something from you, has robbed you of something very precious, you feel enormous anger. Throughout those first two years I had all this anger coming out, and I would be suddenly overwhelmed by it. I didn't know where it was coming from, and it was frightening at times. My poor family! Even now I occasionally feel myself becoming irrationally angry and I have to ask myself where this anger is coming from.

After a few months, Edward said that he thought I should stop talking with Yvonne as she was dragging me down. I was telling her all these positive things, but she always had a plausible excuse for not doing something or for denying something. It was very draining. After having gone round in circles a few times with Yvonne, one Gerson patient told her to pull herself together and stop wasting everyone's time. She wanted to shake her and make her wake up. Yvonne was terribly upset, but even that shock treatment didn't work. She was too far down the path she had made. She had chosen it.

There's a whole generation, my generation, who could not talk about incest. Yvonne was among them. Nowadays things are changing: there is a shift in the climate and people can go for help, but there are still many people out there walking around with all this trauma inside.

38

It's an essential part of the detoxification, getting anger out of the system. The damage done to the immune system by trying to repress these things is enormous. They are actually measuring this now, with the science of psycho-immunology. The experts already tell us that stress can cause cancer. Buried experience is one huge stress on the body and the immune system is unable to defend itself. Isn't it interesting that my cancer was growing in my immune system?

It's these things deep inside us that poison us. We need to see psychological cleansing as part of a whole programme of health, both of cure but also of prevention. Detoxification isn't just achieved through diet, but also through cleaning out anger, fear and other blocks.

We bring up our children by constantly telling them not to cry, be angry or show their feelings. So we bottle up our emotions because it is not nice to show them. Rage is taboo, and must be extinguished as quickly as possible. We don't see it as being a healthy expression, a means to holistic health.

Yvonne was childlike in some ways. After she saw Dr John, I wondered what else I could do to help her, but she was intent on her own destruction. Anna was one of the people who was drawn into Yvonne's circle of fear. She visited her in the hospice and I told her that I thought she was very silly to go and see her if she wanted to get better herself. It horrified Anna how much Yvonne looked like a skeleton. Her eyes and face were sunken and she said, 'It wasn't Yvonne any more. It was just a shell.' By that time Yvonne was on a lot of morphine. All this had a very negative effect on Anna. Much against other people's advice, she went to Yvonne's funeral. It was almost as if she was trying to get sucked into this negativity. I said to her at the time that it wasn't being disloyal in any way not to go, and she had to think about the negative effect that it was going to have on her. But Anna felt she had to go. We had only been on the therapy for a year at that point and it was not something I would have done. I wasn't being disrespectful, I just knew that it could have a negative effect on my healing. But Yvonne's death made me very sad and I did cry a lot afterwards. It was almost as though I was crying for myself because I could see that it could easily have been my funeral, there were so many parallels.

What Yvonne couldn't see was that you have to find your faith for yourself – you can't get it from someone else. People felt drained of their energy after talking to her – what it must have been like for George twenty-four hours a day I can't imagine. She was going round in circles and was totally blocked. It must have been a terrible strain on him. She treated George like a lapdog as far as I could tell. This poor man was going round in ever decreasing circles looking for solutions. Her fear was projected on to him and it must have infected him. It created a downward spiral.

I can remember her saying to me that she had lots of beautiful things in her home and could not bear to leave them behind. I thought, 'My God, why are you thinking about material things? Why?' Yet I used to be like that before I saw Dr John. It was almost as if buying and having things made up for something. But it doesn't. It was a comfort, like food or alcohol. Sometimes, even though I couldn't afford it, I would go out and buy *something*. But it always had to be something bigger and better the next time. I was being driven by an appetite which is never satisfied, always preoccupied with material things.

Perhaps that was a lesson I had to learn. I've always been anxious about not having enough money and suddenly we had a reasonable amount when Edward's parents died. I have had to spend it to keep myself alive. At the beginning it went against the grain. Perhaps that's why I married Edward – money doesn't mean anything to him and he could not understand why I felt guilty about all this money going on me. He didn't see it: 'it's only money!' he'd say. It was a big lesson – wanting to hold on to money is a security blanket. I've had to learn to trust. Edward is a great optimist: he always believes that something will present itself. But for me enough was never enough, so I was always having to have things I didn't really need.

When you are faced with death, you realize that possessions don't mean a thing. You can have all the things in the world, but if you are not going to be here, what difference does it make anyway? I felt guilty for my children's sake about spending all this money. ('They're not going to be able to have this and that and the other if all this is going on me.') But I realized from what they said that they would rather have me than all the money and all the things it could have bought. They seemed quite amazed that I could possibly think like that, but I did.

Yvonne said that it was as if she'd reached a point in her life where she'd got everything she wanted and suddenly somebody came along and said that it was all going to be taken away. Subconsciously she was saying, 'I don't deserve all this and I've got to make sure I don't get it.' And this is precisely what she did do. It's the 'nocebo' again: if you say to yourself that you're going to die, then die you do. Conversely, positivity is very powerful too, and *that's* what you have to tap into. In my opinion it is more powerful, but also more difficult to reach. Negativity is easy to root out; that's there all the time. But you have to cut through it to get to the positive, and that's the difficult bit. But when you do, all the negative stuff dissolves.

39

There were so many similarities in our stories, even to the extent that she had married quite late, as I had. I had been looking for something perfect. I know that I was the cause of the break-up of my previous relationships because I could not give those inner bits of myself that had been repressed. People I was close to found it difficult to cope with those bits I kept to myself. I was constantly searching for something better all the time.

Yvonne kept herself very independent, never gave herself away totally until her late marriage. She talked about the incest in a very matter-of-fact way as if talking about someone else. She didn't actually say to me that she had been 'abused'. She said that she had had an incestuous relationship with her father. So she couldn't bring herself to recognize that it was abuse. Rationally she knew it was, but it was a painful thing to express so she didn't use the word. She had not begun to deal with it; she hadn't even scratched the surface. She thought that because she could talk about it in a detached way, and that she had told George, that was all she needed to do. I can remember her saying to me when I had said how my relationship with Jake had been suppressed, 'I know all about mine, I've dealt with it', but she had not dealt with it at all. She had told George and that was all.

George was a father-figure to her. She was still a child: her emotional development stopped when she was traumatized. She found this very solid, lovely, reliable character and gave him the father status within their relationship. She felt very safe in it and could therefore tell him about her real father. That was the drama they were playing.

I certainly played the little girl role for a long, long time – I'm only just starting to break free of it now. Incest disempowers you, so how can you become a woman? It blocks the maturing process until it is dealt with. Having a terminal illness brings back all the feelings of the abuse: you are suddenly in this powerless situation again. The feelings that you had then are suddenly back again: a different situation, but the same feelings of being powerless to do anything about it. You get carried along on a conveyer belt of doctors and hospitals and scans that increases your feeling of powerlessness. It's the same passive thing: you are lying there and somebody is doing to you something over which you have no control. Maybe Yvonne felt powerless in her illness and thought, 'Well, I was powerless then, so I'm powerless now.'

40

I found it extraordinary that Yvonne was so out of touch with herself, both physically and spiritually, because her life was spent in working with her body. The fact is that she lost control the minute she found her lump. She told me on a few occasions that she could not meditate any more. So it was all no help to her; all her work on her body had been her way of keeping things at bay. Far from being in touch with the centre of her being, she was in no way in touch with anything. It was a mask. This brings me back to the fact that the unconscious mind controls us the whole time. Our conscious wishes are only the tip of the iceberg, just floating around on the top.

Sometime in the next millennium all these ideas about the intricate complexities of the body-mind connections will be taken on board and accepted as part of healing, health and medicine. The human psyche has been mapped during this century, its science is being developed and charted, but wholeness is still mostly ignored. People still don't want to look at themselves in their entirety.

There was Yvonne, with all her material advantages and possessions, yet these horrible things from the past kept coming up and nibbling away at her security. However much she had consciously tried to get rid of them, they just wouldn't go. Her beautiful home was a safe place for her, and she tried to keep everything out. ('If I build these walls and hide here, nothing can come through them.') When we moved house, one of the first things I did was to build a wall in the garden between us and our neighbours. It was exactly what I did emotionally as well. But it didn't keep the feelings out as they were inside me all the time. You can't *keep* it out – you need to *get* it out! I was always having these fantasies that if I went somewhere or did something, then everything would be all right, but the fact is that you take your feelings with you!

She regarded her home as very lovely, beautifully decorated, with lots of money put into it. She couldn't see that those things were nothing, even when she was at the brink. Lots of people can't; that's the sad thing. Or they can see it, but it's too painful to acknowledge. It is easier to die, to opt out. Facing life is more difficult than accepting death. Facing up to who you are is the hardest thing of all.

I said that to Dr John: 'Supposing I don't like me when I've done this!'

He told me a story.

'When we are born, we go off down the path of our life. Then things happen to us – traumas, abuse, whatever material is given to us. So we start veering off the path, we go down another one. Because it is not our true path, our true path is elsewhere, we have an inner conflict. Part of us wants the true path and part of us is going off at a tangent. We are always having to wear a mask. It is not who we really are; it is somebody else. The damage to the immune system because of all the emotional energy that is being used to keep us going down this wrong path and keeping up pretences is immense. We learn patterns of behaviour to accommodate this veering off, to protect ourselves. We are going further and further away from who we really are, so there is a desperate conflict between who we really are and the masks we wear. Finally we begin to identify with the masks, and we think it's the real us. We forget the other.

'It depends how much fuel you give in your life to the true path, whether the spark and the flame are kept alive. If you are completely identified with the material world, then that flame will die, or it becomes so distant that you can't access it. The problem is that we may be able to see this as adults, but the feelings that got locked up by the child, those repressed feelings, protected us as children, making life bearable. We pushed them to the back because they were so horrible that we couldn't think about them. They were repressed to help us to cope with life. Yet those same things come back.

'So you can look at it like this: the material we are given as children is ours to work on when we are adults. That is our chance of growth.'

41

Our personal evolution depends on how we deal with our life material. Everybody has their problems. A lot of people think 'poor me, it doesn't happen to anyone else', but everybody has their life material to deal with. It's a question of what you do with it. When you think of how repressed feelings must be tied up with *survival* for the child, dealing with them in later life *also* presents a matter of life and death. You have to make a choice.

People used to say to me that I looked so aloof. They thought I was so in control, yet inside I didn't feel like that at all. The mask I had on was of someone in total control. So we present the opposite face to how we really feel, and often tell other people to do the things we need to do ourselves.

Possibly Yvonne was like that. She seemed successful, rich, attractive and in touch with herself, but inside she was the opposite. I can relate to that; it was just how I was. Even down to the 'if I have material things and wealth, I must be good, I must go up in everyone's estimation and I'm not the worthless person that I thought I was. I have all these things, how can I be worthless?'.

What frightened me was what would happen if I didn't like the real me when I found out who I was. That really scared me. Supposing it went against my lifestyle, what was I going to do? That's another reason why we find it so difficult to look at ourselves; it threatens all the things that we have. Perhaps Yvonne would have found that she didn't want to live in her flat, she didn't need her beautiful things, she didn't need George, because the person that needed him wasn't really her. That is scary, very scary. You have built your whole life on certain foundations, and suddenly you question everything you've ever done.

I asked Dr John, 'What if I no longer want my family or my

husband?' He replied, 'Well, that's a chance you have to take. But I don't think you will. You have to step out into the unknown; that's what it's all about, taking the risk. No one can do that for you.'

It infuriated me at the time. I thought why couldn't this bloody man tell me what to do instead of this constant 'don't ask me'! Particularly since he was a doctor! But you have to find your own truth.

Yvonne was venting her anger on George, displaced anger which she called love. ('If I am going to suffer, then you're going to come with me, my love.') At some level she was punishing her father, but because she hadn't dealt with the incest, it was George who suffered. It's a dreadful punishment: almost as if she wanted him to die as well, to take him with her. The ultimate revenge, the ultimate blackmail. She was a tragic figure.

42

When imagination and desire work together, then anything is possible. But if they are in conflict, then imagination will always win. So no matter whether you are facing death and wanting to live, the imagination – even in the unconscious – will quash the desire if they are in conflict.

In Yvonne's case, her desire to live was overruled by her subconscious 'imagination'. Her unresolved trauma caused a drama to be acted out deep down, and she carried it through into adult life without having resolved it. She never found out how to release the trauma through talking about it, facing it, feeling it, working through it. That's when it loses its power. Then there is no conflict any more and it disappears.

Because this conflict is raging, you lose energy all the time in fighting the battle that is going on in your mind. The energy required for this is enormous. It damages the immune system as your ability to use that energy for helping your body is locked away doing something else. Yvonne was a prime example of this because she was using all her energy in order to carry on the drama, but only fuelling the conflict. Her energy wasn't being used in a positive way, and was going to the wrong places.

I discussed this with someone whose husband is having the therapy. She told me 'When I met my husband thirty or forty years ago he was a free spirit. He wanted to travel, but we fell in love and his subconscious desire was squashed by falling in love. So we married and had children.'

She said that she could see, over the years, his yearning for the things he hadn't had and she believed that that was where his cancer had come from. He had cancer in the gut – a classic conflict between conscious desire and the unconscious mind.

The answer is to resolve these conflicts within yourself, become aware of them, release them and then use that resolution to positive effect in your life. This brings up the whole question of therapy. I'm terribly aware of the therapy trap and I see people going around in circles, endlessly tying themselves in mental knots, because they are not working at any level other than the intellectual. There are other factors, and we have to clean out the body as well as the mind. Alice Miller has actually said, 'Childhood experience is stored in the *cells*.'

You could say that 'good' therapy is a good preventive measure, but that calls into question what therapy is. It seems to me that a lot of people, both clients and therapists, haven't clearly defined therapy for themselves. Therapy deals with the individual Self, the Ego-self. It doesn't, to start with, deal with the transcendent self or soul, so let's make the distinction between Ego-self and soul. What therapy can do is to clean up the Ego-self, because we get in a muddle with all our life experiences. There is much hidden material that needs to be cleaned up at a certain point in one's journey so that one can see more clearly the transcendent self, the soul.

Often therapy doesn't recognize this distinction, and doesn't even allow for the existence of the soul. Analysis can be pure escapism. This is a major danger when you are dealing with illness or health, therapeutically or as a preventive, because you may be pushing things further and further underground, while getting caught in the traps of dependence, transference and power, going round in circles and never breaking through, let alone reaching the transcendent self.

I was lucky to find Dr John. I have been to another hypnotherapist since, and it wasn't the same at all. I was very disappointed. There are very few really good practitioners around. Dr John felt that psychoanalysis was a total waste of time – you spend years getting to know your problem inside out, but you don't know the solution to it. It's all on a rational level, not on an emotional or spiritual level.

It is one thing seeing things that have happened to you in your life, and talking about them, but it is another thing *feeling* them, feeling that pain from long ago. Yvonne was a classic example: she could talk about it, but she couldn't feel it. She was skimming the surface the whole time. It's the feelings that are the painful bit.

Alice Miller has now disowned psychoanalysis – she says it's a con, a lot of people making a lot of money. Dr John said exactly the same thing to me: he did not believe in traditional psychoanalysis. You just keep talking round things, because the feelings aren't coming up. That's why people go into analysis for years and years, talking about why they are doing what they are doing, but it doesn't help them with the feelings. The feelings have to be exorcized, felt, not just talked about. You have to re-enter the experience. With hypnotherapy, the feelings came up immediately. Remembering the details of the experience is not important; it's releasing the feelings that go with the experience that is the crucial part of the treatment.

Few therapists seem to make the soul connection, yet without the transpersonal element you are dealing with symptoms; you are not dealing with the whole picture. It is important to differentiate between personality and soul. Who you really are is not necessarily what you have become. It's getting in touch with that reality, with the source, and finding out who you really are that is incredibly exciting. It opens up amazing possibilities.

43

In the West we see illness as something negative, not as a positive thing. When I could see that my illness *was* positive, it was the most wonderful thing that had ever happened to me: embracing my cancer and loving it. Without that insight, I would have just gone stumbling along as before, and ultimately I would have died. The only way I got that insight was through the illness, so illness can be something very positive.

In our culture, symptoms have to be eradicated. We don't look at what is the cause of the illness, just the symptoms. There will be both logical *and* analogical causes; the two things go together. It's not 'either/or', it's 'both/and'. Orthodox medicine just looks at a segment, a part, and deals with it as best it can. Orthodox practitioners think that the spirit and the mind are separate from the body, that they are not connected in any way. Yet they send out mixed messages: they say on the one hand if you suffer from stress it is mind and spirit that cause the physical problem, but they will not take the argument a step further.

Psycho-immunology is now an established area of science. Stress, bereavement and shock are scientifically proven to cause illness. Research scientists (*see* Further Reading) have measured the white blood cells and they do not do their job after these events. But nobody is allowing their minds to work laterally, to unveil underlying universal principles.

Yvonne was subconsciously telling herself that she was going to die. Her immune system packed up. Researchers (*see* Further Reading) know this power of the mind from experiments under hypnosis: they tell someone that they are going to be burned by something very hot. They say, 'It's going on your arm now,' and they touch the person with a pencil, and within seconds blisters appear. These experiments are documented. That chemical message goes from the brain to the body, producing a blister when the subject has only been touched by a pencil: that proves that it's not the contact with the object alone that causes damage to the body.

When I first went to see Dr John, he gave me a book called *The Causes and Prevention of Cancer*. Levenson believed that you could cure anything with the mind. Dr John said to me that we know virtually every single thing there is to know about the body, ninety-nine per cent of the biochemistry and the rest, but when it comes to the mind we most probably know about two per cent. We have only just scratched the surface of the mind. A lot of neurologists and brain specialists are the first to admit that they are working with only theories most of the time as far as the mind is concerned.

It's an incredibly exciting science to explore now for the next millennium. There are routes already mapped, both in psycho-immunology and hypnosis, but there's also a place in medical training for looking at the whole picture, and examining other underlying principles of diagnosis and treatment. We need to open our minds.

PART 4

A New Life

The difference from a person and an angel is easy. Most of an angel is in the inside and most of a person is on the outside.

MR GOD, THIS IS ANNA

44

When I got back from Mexico, I had a letter from Dr Allan the nutritionist, saying, 'You came to see me six months ago, how are you getting on? Perhaps you'd like to get in touch.'

I telephoned him and he was very surprised to hear me. He had never expected, he told me later, to get a reply. He has kept in touch ever since because he has become extremely interested in my case.

I went to see him again and he did a whole series of nutritional tests, like the ones he had done when I was diagnosed. Before he did them he said to me, 'On what you are eating, you are going to be even more deficient than you were.'

He rang me up later: 'I've just got the results of your tests: I'm afraid I have to eat my words! Your zinc and red cell magnesium are now normal!' He was, in the cautious way that doctors are, quite excited about it. He asked if I minded if he contacted Professor Stellart. I said no, not at all. He later told me that when he had contacted him, the Professor had told him that when he had said to me, 'You'll be dead before you can finish the therapy,' he was actually giving me considerably less time than that. A few months at most. He was very surprised that I was still alive.

However, he didn't want to see me. He would keep in touch through Dr Allan. He was going to follow my case, but he didn't want to be seen to get too involved.

When you're really ill and facing death you find out who your friends are. While I was in the clinic, Caroline was a mother to the children. She supported them emotionally, as well as giving them a good time and looking after them. People who were nothing more than acquaintances, like my friend who drove me to the surgery the day of my diagnosis, suddenly appeared to scrub carrots, wash lettuces, make juices and allow me to sit down, whereas other people who I thought were my friends suddenly disappeared. In some ways it was hurtful, but when someone you know is terminally ill, it brings you face to face with your own mortality. And when you're on a radical therapy that some people think is a waste of time, they don't know how to handle it.

Because of the path I had chosen, I couldn't go to dinner parties, so I was not 'one of them' any more. It shows you how sincere some people are and how others are not. You realize how some people *do* care, and others profess to care, but when push comes to shove they don't. One couple we saw regularly disappeared completely. They never even rang. We thought we were close to them, but they showed that they didn't really care at all.

I continued on the therapy and life went on. At the end of 1991, over Christmas, I hadn't been feeling too bad, so we went out to a neighbour's party for New Year's Eve. I decided I was well enough to go – I had been on the therapy for nine months and I was feeling fine. But by the time I got back, I could feel myself sinking, both mentally and physically.

For those first three weeks of January 1992 I felt very depressed and terribly weepy. I was saying to my friends, 'This is it, I'm sure I'm going to die now.' It was the total opposite to how I had been: even through all the times of feeling bad I had always been very positive. Suddenly I became very morose, lethargic and disheart-ened, and quite aggressive. I had terrible rages when anger was coming out of me all the time. I would cry with rage, go upstairs and punch the pillow with my fist, not knowing where all this anger was coming from. At Sunday lunch one of the children said something derogatory about the meal. I was holding a saucepan full of vegetables and I threw the whole lot across the floor. Everyone was horrified. I stormed out and slammed the door, shaking with rage. It was frightening, because this rage was coming from somewhere deep inside, and I couldn't handle it. I didn't know what was happening. it was misdirected rage: it wasn't for the people who were getting it, but they were taking the brunt. I could hear Edward saying to the children, 'It's all right, it's just part of Mummy's illness. She's not angry with you. It's something she's going through.'

Considering he was on the receiving end of a lot of my anger, he was wonderful. Sometimes I was so hurtful, I would even scream at him, 'I don't know why I ever married you.'

I could feel huge amounts of anger coming out of me. Really it was not like me at all. Another time I went and hid and nobody could find me. I sat there and could hear the children's voices getting frantic ('Mummy, where are you?') while I was sitting there seething with rage. I didn't know why – it wasn't something specific, it was old rage.

I felt rotten all month, physically and mentally very low. Then on Saturday 25 January I went to bed, having been irritable and bad-tempered all day, feeling strange and not too good at all. I woke up and looked at the clock. It was three o'clock. I had this incredible, immense burning pain coming from above my navel up through my chest. Although it was awful in one way, somehow I knew it was good. It was a huge healing reaction. I could feel something dissolving inside. I woke Edward, and we lay there awestruck. We had our hands together on my abdomen and we could feel this immense heat coming from inside. It lasted for about an hour, which was similar to the initial one I'd had in Mexico. The extraordinary thing was that it was exactly the same time of night, at 3 am when, I later learned, the liver is at its most active. I said to him, 'Something's happening, but I know it's something good.'

You know instinctively that it's something positive that's happening, just as when I had chemotherapy I knew that what was happening was something really bad. You just know.

It wasn't pain, but it was a sensation, right from my navel through my chest, of amazing heat coming deep from inside. It wasn't frightening because we both knew that something incredible was happening, that my body was repairing itself. It was really exciting.

When I woke on Sunday morning I had a bad headache. But the gland in my armpit had shrunk almost completely away. I'd had this huge swelling the size of a melon under my arm, to the extent that I didn't have to raise my arm for anyone to see it. You could see it bulging from underneath. It had completely gone.

I took an enema and the headache disappeared. Whatever toxins had been broken down from this huge healing reaction were cleaned out, because over the next few weeks I felt better and better, and my energy levels went up and up. When my blood test was taken at the end of February, my white cell count had gone from 4.3 to 9.4. My immune system was starting to function again. My white cells increased up to 12 point something. My immune system had gone into overdrive. It was as if, by my body dissolving this tumour, the big blockage in the sewer had finally been sucked out and suddenly everything started to function again.

45

It was from that point that my body started to recover. I did have bad times over the next eighteen months, but that was the big healing crisis. The depression in January was a classic healing sign: you feel very weepy, but the trouble is that when you're in it yourself all you can see is the gloom and the doom and you can't see your way out of it.

Dr Sanchez told me that depression was very common in healing crises and that it was the time when people got most disheartened, because of toxins going round in the brain. People often stopped the therapy just when they were on the point of breakthrough, and I can understand that. Looking back at how I was, I was very depressed. But I never thought of giving up the therapy. I had this inner strength: whatever had happened to me in hypnotherapy, it was *that* that kept me going. But I can see how easy it is to give up at this time, because you think, 'This can't be working, otherwise why do I feel this bad?'

When I talk to people now and they say how bad they feel, I beg them not to give up, and tell them that when it passes, they will suddenly feel wonderful. It's an amazing experience. But it's almost as if you have to go right down into the pit before you can rise again, like the proverbial phoenix from the ashes. I did have healing crises after that, but that was the big one. It was very significant. The one in Mexico had been under the navel, and this one was further up, it was from the solar plexus going right up into my chest.

After that, my mood lifted. It was as if something had dissolved inside, as something most definitely had. The large tumours in my abdomen had gone. I know from the letters from St Lucy's to my GP, and from the scans, that that was where the disease had been at its worst. The fact is that my white blood cell count showed that something amazing had happened inside. It had swept away the disease and with it got washed away all the other toxins in the system.

Through 1992 and 1993 life carried on in a fairly monotonous way. All the time I was looking more and more at myself, looking at why I had done things and how they had affected me. So as well as a physical cleaning, I was carrying on the journey inwards at the same time, while still doing the Gerson therapy. Since the healing crisis, my energy had increased enormously, I'd got my white blood cells back and I was feeling much better. However, all the lymph nodes in my neck and my groin and my armpits were still swollen and I could feel all these little tumours in the lymphatic system.

I was in regular touch with the clinic in Mexico. Dr Sanchez told me that the body is very clever and will deal with the most urgent things first.

'Don't worry about the superficial nodes on the surface because those aren't the ones that will kill you, it's the ones deep inside the body which will kill you,' she said. 'You could have two tumours side by side and the body will deal with the one that is most life-threatening and leave the other one.'

They have actually seen that happen. People who suffer from arthritis and diabetes find that eventually these conditions go too. They are all degenerative diseases and, if you are giving the body the right fuel as it heals one thing, it will go on to heal those other conditions.

This gave me a whole new perspective on my body and it made me treat it with far more respect. What a wonderful thing it is, and how we abuse it. We are so ignorant and it is so wise. During that huge healing reaction, Edward and I were lying there in total awe of this wonderful thing that was happening, something we could not control at all. It was absolutely fantastic. People forget that, even with orthodox medicine, doctors administer their treatment but it's the body that actually does the healing. No one else can do that for us. If the body is cut open for an operation, the doctors stitch it up, but the body heals itself.

We lose that awareness, and we give our responsibility away. But once you can take full responsibility, the body is capable of doing anything. You have to have immense faith in it, because some of the things the body does to get to that point of healing are very hard to comprehend. I felt so ill while it was doing them. If you can only have faith in yourself, your body can do it. It *will* be all right in the end, because we have this inner knowledge. Dr John showed me how to trust in that. Trust in your instincts and not in your rational mind. He said to me, 'Always follow your instincts because that is the truth, that's what's coming from inside.'

We don't use our instincts any more; we distrust them the whole time. But that's what has kept me going all through this – even when things were bad, this little voice from deep inside kept saying, 'It's going to be all right if you just keep going,' even though everyone around me was saying otherwise. If you can get in touch with that inner strength it is so wonderful.

Hans J Eysenck, one of the world's most cited psychologists and a pioneer in the uses of behavioural therapy, talks about the Type A and Type B personalities. Type B is the doormat type, the cancer-prone individual whose relationship with cancer is very strongly recorded. I was the typical cancer personality – but it wasn't *me*. Not the *real* me. The trauma that happened to me as a child turned me from my path, from my real self, into this helpless, hopeless person who was cancer-prone. The most exciting thing for people is that they might not really be the person they think they are – in fact, they most certainly are not!

46

Everything was fine for a period of eighteen months, although the superficial lymph nodes on the surface were still not budging. So in the autumn of 1993 I spoke to Dr Sanchez on the phone and he said, 'We are going to put you back on the intensive therapy to see if we can give a push to the body to get rid of this stuff still in the lymph nodes. We are also going to give you castor oil by mouth.'

I was at this time down to ten juices and three enemas a day. I had not had castor oil before, because it can be too much for the liver suddenly to have all these toxins flooding out if you have had even the tiniest amount of chemotherapy. Dr Sanchez thought that after two years of detoxification my body would be strong enough to take it.

There was a slow deterioration at that point, so I went back on the intensive therapy. By the end of 1993 I was having castor oil every other day and 13 juices plus five enemas – including castor oil enemas. Castor oil is another aspect of the Gerson therapy:

because it is a poison to the body, all the body wants to do is to get rid of it as quickly as possible. It acts a bit like a broom – it goes through and pulls everything off the walls and takes it out with it. So it is wonderfully cleansing for the body, even though it is the most gruesome thing to take. It certainly has a dramatic effect on the body.

It may be that after two years of detoxifying it was too much for my body, because by the end of 1993 I was slowly starting to react. My ankles started to swell, then my legs, and my knees, and then the upper parts of my legs and my abdomen. By the end of the year I could hardly walk because my legs were so swollen. I didn't feel particularly ill but my body was swelling and swelling. I got to the stage when I could hardly walk up the stairs because I had so much fluid inside me and I couldn't breathe properly. Something was obviously not right.

I decided to go back to St Lucy's and have a scan. Even though the lesions from my liver had gone, the disease was still active in my lymph glands. I had the scan at Dr Sanchez's instigation, as she wanted to see what was happening. I rang Professor Stellart because he was the only person who could arrange it. He was charm itself. ('Oh yes, my dear, you can come and have a scan.') There was no mention of the fact that three years previously he had told me I would die if I didn't have chemotherapy. It was as if it hadn't happened.

When I went back to get the results, Professor Stellart was awful to me. I sat in the waiting room feeling very confident, looking at all these people looking so ill and grey, and I thought, 'Gosh, I would be doing this. I would have spent these last three years going backwards and forwards, having chemicals poured into me and leading this horrible life.'

As I was sitting there, he came out dressed in his usual dandyish way. Although he saw me, he chose not to acknow-ledge me. He put on a little show for my benefit, going up and putting his arm round his patients. ('Oh, hello Mrs So-and-so, how are you? You do look well.') They kept me waiting about an hour. Then the woman consultant called me in and I asked her if she had my scan results because all I had asked them to do was a scan so that I could send it to Mexico. She ignored me and said, 'Right now, what I propose that we do is to start off with some chemotherapy.'

I sat there and wondered what was happening. I was supposed

to be here picking up my scan results. So I said, 'Hang on, where is my scan?'

'Oh, there are still swollen glands, so we are going to do various treatments.'

'Hang on! I am not here for treatment. I don't want any advice. All I want is the scan.'

She was quite taken aback.

'Do you mind if I examine you?'

I now wish I had refused, but I agreed and so she examined me.

'There are one or two lymph nodes still swollen.'

'Yes, I know.'

I then said to her, 'Can I have the scan?'

'Just a moment.'

And she went off. She came back with Professor Stellart who was furious with me. His face was full of anger. ('How dare this woman come back a second time, alive, not having died as I told her she was going to, and demand her scan and then be off!') He was fuming. He could hardly bring himself to look at me, he was so angry.

I said, 'I want my scan results.'

'We haven't got them.'

'You *must* have them!'

'Well, it's on the screen but we haven't got it in print.'

'I want it.'

'You can't have it now, we haven't got it.'

I got up and walked out. I was so angry. I had gone there feeling positive, and went home on the train, still without the scan result, seething with anger that they should treat me like that. I had gone up to London, sat there for an hour, and they hadn't given it to me.

Edward said to me, '*Why* don't they want you to see these scan results? *Why* won't they give them to you? There must be a reason. Did you ever see the original scan results?'

'No, I didn't actually *see* them.'

'I think you should ask for them so that you can compare them.'

I rang up Professor Stellart's secretary next morning and said, 'You are supposed to be sending me some scan results.'

'Oh, yes.'

'Well, I would like the original scan results as well.'

'Oh.'

I put the phone down. I wasn't sure if I was going to get them, but I did. The original scan showed two lesions on the liver that were not on the second scan. I wondered whether this was why they hadn't wanted to show me. I can't prove it. However, the scan report dated 5 November 1993 said:

> Scans were compared with the previous examination dated October 1990. There has been a marked deterioration. There are massively enlarged bilateral axillary node. (*sic*) No significant hilar or mediastinal lymph node enlargement.
>
> The spleen is slightly enlarged and has, I think, increased since the previous scan. There are massively enlarged para-aortic, peri-pancreatic, lymph nodes. The liver and kidneys appear normal. It is difficult to separate the pancreas from the surrounding lymphadenopathy.
>
> Extensive disease recurrence.

47

At the end of January I had a blood test. I then got a letter from my GP saying that there was obviously something dramatically wrong with my body. Whatever I was doing was not working. My haemoglobin had dropped and there were lots of other signs that things weren't good. I could hardly breathe because I was retaining so much fluid. It was a deep crisis point.

> I scanned your blood results recently and it is clear at a glance that your condition is deteriorating. I am well aware of your feelings about non-conventional therapy, but I feel it my responsibility to point out to you that it seems that this alternative path that you have chosen is not 'working' at the moment. Your blood count is down to 8 (haemoglobin) which is only two-thirds of circulating blood that is desirable. The cholesterol is very low, which is a marker for severe disease. The liver enzymes are raised, indicating disease activity and the blood protein levels are denoting disease activity.
>
> It is my personal opinion that you would be wise to return to conventional therapy. I have no desire for the past to repeat itself. If you are happy with your current situation, then so be it. If you wish to be reviewed at St Lucy's, please come and consult.

When I saw his letter I was faced with a decision: what was I going to do? Dr Sanchez could not understand what was going on. She thought that the lymphoma must for some reason be taking hold

again. Everyone was telling me that I should go and have chemotherapy, and that it was the only solution. For a very short time –
and it most probably was only for an hour – I thought, *'this is it.'*
At this point I actually said to the children, 'I am going to die. This
is it.' They could not believe it. They were wonderful: they kept
saying to me, 'Please don't give up, please just keep going, please.'
They pleaded with me. The eldest and the youngest both said,
'Please, Mummy, please go on with what you are doing.'

The middle one is very practical and down to earth and said,
'Well, I think you should have whatever is going to keep you
alive and if that needs chemotherapy, well, I think you should
have it.'

He was unemotional; the others were showing their true feelings. Edward was very scared at this point. He said, 'I think you
should do whatever you think you should do, and I'm not going
to influence you. You have done the right thing up till now.'

I knew that they were right, but there were all these people
around me telling me to have chemotherapy. Nobody could
understand what was happening.

Ever since I made that connection with Dr John during the
hypnotherapy session I had had this enormous inner strength that
I didn't even have to think about; it was just there. It was what
kept me going through it all. I wish I could explain it, but I can't
– it was just an amazing feeling that I wasn't going to die. I just
had to keep on going down the path I was following and ultimately I was going to be all right.

Although that feeling never really left me, at the same time I
started to doubt, and fears started to creep in. I could see what
was happening to my body, and then suddenly I saw it written
down in black and white. When you *read* it, you have to face it.

I started frantically phoning everybody. The first person I spoke
to was Dr Allan in London. I felt that my own GP was biased – he
wanted me to have chemotherapy, and I wasn't going to listen to
him, so I would go to Dr Allan who would be much more
open-minded about it. He turned around and said, 'No, I agree
with your GP. I believe that the reason why your legs are so
swollen is that the lymphoma in your abdomen, in your stomach
where the disease is at its worst, are becoming so large that they
are pressing on the blood supply down to the legs which is
causing the swelling, and you should think very seriously about
chemotherapy.'

A friend came up to look after me because I was in such a bad way. I was very weepy at this point, and I just couldn't cope. She brought me up some juice in bed, and I started to cry. 'I am so grateful that you are doing this for me,' I said, as if I couldn't accept that she would want to do it for me.

She replied, 'You have always found it difficult to accept friendship and love in the spirit in which it is intended. You are always thinking that you have to repay somebody for anything that is done for you.'

It was to do with the feeling of not deserving it: why should anyone want to do this for me?

Then I got a terrible metallic taste in my mouth, really strong. I was desperate. Nobody seemed able to help me, so I rang Charlotte Gerson. Perhaps it was a coincidence, but I couldn't get hold of her. She most probably would have pulled me back on course, but I actually needed to do it myself. I spoke to the Gerson research organization, told them what the problem was and they said, 'We can't understand what is happening. We haven't seen this before. Have you thought about chemotherapy?'

I could not believe this. What was this man saying to me? I had been doing this therapy for two and a half years and now he was telling me to have chemotherapy. I was so angry with him. I said, 'There is *no way* I am having chemotherapy.'

Then I spoke to Dr Sanchez, and she said, 'Perhaps you should have some chemotherapy. No reason to come off the therapy, but . . .'

I was totally stunned. It was just like someone chopping my feet off from underneath me. I could not believe it. I was asking all these people's advice because I wanted someone to say to me, no, you don't need chemotherapy. But they were *all* telling me I needed it.

Then the research people rang me back and said that I might have castor oil poisoning. Immediately, I knew. After two years of cleansing and suddenly being given two tablespoons of castor oil every other day, it was poisoning my system. I had been saying all along that since I'd had castor oil that I had been deteriorating. But everyone kept saying to me that no one had ever had this problem before! In the same way you can give a drug to a thousand people and you might just get one who reacts. I knew that I had a very sensitive body. When I had chemotherapy and had hallucinations, St Lucy's told me they had never known anyone have this problem before! My instinct had been saying to me that the castor oil was causing the problems, but I was allowing their rationality to negate my own feelings.

48

I was still panic-stricken, rushing about like a headless chicken, asking everyone what I should do, getting conflicting advice from everyone and feeling very negative. I phoned a fellow-patient who mentioned a book by Stephen Levine. I hadn't got the book he mentioned, although I knew I had one of his books somewhere. We talked a lot about other things, but when I put the phone down, for some reason I remembered this book. I went through my books and found it. I had bought it, flicked through it, and stuck it on a shelf, mainly because on the Gerson therapy I hadn't had time to read it. There it was, but I had never looked at it. I picked it up and it opened at a particular page. It was amazing. I read this:

> BE YOUR OWN FOOL. Trust your process. No one knows what needs to be done for your healing better than you. Kabir says, we have ways within each of us which will never be known by anyone. Trust these ways. You are the path. Don't be someone else's fool. Buddha's. Moses'. Mary's. Treat yourself lightly. The comparing mind often attempts to adjust the compass, and navigate by another's stars. And we become lost. Be your own fool. Walk nobody's path but your own. Trust your vision and be a lamp unto yourself.

This was exactly what I needed to get me back on to my own path, to trust the instincts that had guided me so well over the past three years. So now I tell people to trust their own instincts, not someone else's. You will always be guided on the path right for you.

Reading *The Celestine Prophecy* and thinking about coincidences, it was amazing that my friend mentioned the book, that I opened it up at that page, and there, at that moment, was the answer I had been looking for. Trust yourself; don't listen to anyone else. My instinct said, 'Go on with what you are doing. No chemotherapy. But you need some help from somewhere.'

It was amazing – the fact that it was a book I hadn't even read. I just opened it and there were the answers, all of them, inside me. Just trust in them. That, unfortunately, is what Yvonne couldn't do. But I couldn't have done, either, before Dr John.

I stopped the castor oil and my body went down slightly, but not that significantly. I was quite perturbed because by this point it really was affecting me. I had very limited mobility, I could hardly walk, and I had to lie down most of the time with my legs up because they were so swollen. So I decided that I needed to talk to someone who could *see* me – Dr Sanchez was too far away, so she couldn't see what was happening to my body. I did in fact contemplate going back to Mexico, but when I spoke to Dr Sanchez, she didn't think I was in any fit state to travel, and that it could give me more problems than I already had.

Then I thought about going to a Gerson clinic in Germany, but finally decided to go to a local naturopath. He was very sympathetic to the Gerson therapy and believed that I was doing the right thing. 'But,' he said, 'I think there's too much fluid going into your body – 13 juices a day is too much. I think you've got to not take any juices for two weeks.'

This was horrifying news. I said, 'I don't know if I can do that.'

'Well, that's my opinion; it's up to you whether you choose to take it. That's what I feel.'

He gave me some homoeopathic preparations which would help. I started taking them, and slowly began to cut down on the juices, but I was terrified. For two and a half years these juices had kept me alive, and stopping them felt like cutting off my head.

I called Dr Sanchez in Mexico and told her I had been to see a naturopath and this is what he had advised. She said, 'Good! I think you've done the right thing. He can see what is happening and I can't.'

She was very positive about it. She was as convinced as I was that the castor oil had caused the swelling in my body, but she believed it also would push out the last of the disease.

But it still wasn't shifting. In the end I thought that I just had to do something. I didn't take any juices for a week – no fluid at all into my body, no water, nothing. My naturopath told me not to drink any soup – just a dry diet. It was wonderful! Suddenly, from my life having been dominated by having juices and enemas, I didn't have to do them! And the fluid started to go. Over a period of two or three months it drained off; slowly my abdomen went down, then the legs, past the knees, then the lower legs, and it gradually went. My haemoglobin went up again slowly and things started to return to normal. As it went, all the little lumps went with it! All the tumours disappeared with the fluid.

The lumps on the surface, even though they are not the dangerous ones, are none the less the ones you keep constantly touching,
and are a reminder of the disease. The glands under my arms were
so large at one stage that they were pulsing, beating and throbbing
away. The one under my left armpit was huge, like a grapefruit.
I had them all up my neck, running right up to my skull at the
back, down the sides of my breast, lumps all the way down, right
down both groins. Plus when I lay down I had this huge ball
moving about in my belly, a huge great thing, like a creature
moving around. Suddenly they all disappeared. And from then I
have never looked back.

I gradually went back to six juices, then I slowly reduced it
again and now I drink about three a day. I still see the naturopath
who gives me acupuncture. He tells me that my blood chemistry
still isn't quite right. There are still some things in my blood which
aren't totally normal. I have these skin patches which look like a
rash, and he says that it is the last of the toxins slowly coming out
and that gradually it will return to normal. My white blood cell
count is OK, and the lymph nodes and the glands have all gone
back to normal. It was dramatic.

I am now off all medication, the digestive enzymes and thyroid
tablets and potassium that Gerson prescribes – I've been off all of
those for the past six months, and everything is fine. My
naturopath is still trying to deal with the slight skin problem. I am
still drinking the juices and eating the prescribed food. Dr Sanchez
said that I could start eating fish a couple of times a week, but not
to start eating eggs yet.

I know it has gone. I know. I don't have any worries.

49

I don't know how St Lucy's are going to take it when I go back for
a scan this time. I don't even know whether the Professor will give
me another scan or not. But I have the right as a taxpayer. I haven't
cost the NHS very much so far!

When I came back from Mexico I had to have a blood test every
six weeks. I asked my GP if he was willing to do it on the NHS.

Some GPs wouldn't do it: people I knew were having to pay £120 a time. I had already prepared this speech: if he refused I was going to say to him, 'With the consultants' time, drugs and all the rest of it, how much have I saved the NHS?' Interferon alone is phenomenally expensive. I had my biopsy done privately when I was diagnosed, through Edward's health insurance. When he rang the insurers after the biopsy and told them that it was cancer, they said, 'Oh well, you are much better off having it done on the NHS because that is where the specialists are, but also we wouldn't cover those sorts of costs, they are too high!' The average cancer patient costs hundreds of thousands of pounds in treatment and consultants' time.

It makes me angry because the Gerson therapy has cost us £30,000. Compared to what it would have cost the NHS for me to have had conventional therapy, it's a drop in the ocean. It is most probably one-tenth of the cost. *And* I'm alive! In many cases, if a husband dies, the State then has to support the family, so the cost doesn't end with the death of the person. The cost of cancer is phenomenal. It makes me angry that I couldn't get our health insurance company to pay for it. But they won't.

Stellart's reaction was horrible – so closed-minded, it was inhuman. If you are dying, you can have all their sympathy as long as you play the passive role. Do what you are told and die. They will give you warmth and affection and care because you are going to die. They will tell you how brave you are. ('Takes her chemotherapy, doesn't complain, wonderful patient.') How stupid just to lie there and allow them to do all these things! But perfect patients don't ask any questions and don't do anything for themselves.

The classic response from these closed-minded doctors if a patient recovers is 'perhaps it wasn't diagnosed properly!'. If you get it and you die from it, you had cancer. If you survive, they made a mistake in the first place, even with proof like CT scans – and how can they lie? I heard that in Mexico all the time. This is one of the reasons I was determined to get hold of the scan reports. Or they say that you have had a spontaneous remission. I asked Stellart once, how many spontaneous remissions had he seen. They don't see any, that's the truth. If you survive for five years without treatment, without a recurrence, you are cured. It will be five years in October since I had any treatment. They will find ways of saying that I wasn't diagnosed correctly. But I have the scans to prove it.

The only person who may be on my side is Dr Allan. He did recognize what I had got, and the success of the treatment. My GP is unbelievable. He was very angry because he felt that he had put himself out on a limb to get me into St Lucy's. He saw my action as a slap in the face: he had got me into the best lymphoma hospital around, as he saw it, and what did I do but turn around and say that I didn't want it. I was going to go and eat carrots! He was very angry. In the letter he wrote me when I got ill again, he said 'we don't want a repeat of history'. In other words, if you go back this time, don't you dare slap me in the face again.

He knows my situation: for the last three years, every time I go in for a blood test, he sees me sitting there waiting for the nurse and he will say, 'Oh hello, Eileen' in a very off-hand manner. There is something inside him which is dying to ask, but the other bit of him tells him he must keep me at arm's length. But if Edward goes in, he tells him, 'I do so *admire* your wife!' He would never dream of saying that to me, not in a million years.

When you go into a doctor's surgery, people are sitting there waiting to be summoned. Their control has been taken away. You must not have responsibility for your body. It is not allowed. Doctors enjoy the power trip. In Third World cultures the witch doctor has this mystique about him, and if he tells you that you are going to die before the moon rises, you die. This is the sort of mystique that doctors like to cultivate. Of course, on the positive side it is valuable to have a 'healer archetype'. But I found my healer in *me*. Most people project on to someone else – they need this other person to give them healing because they haven't found that resource within themselves. But it seems that doctors abuse this power and they use it for negative as well as positive purposes, which is constricting for proper healing.

They talk in language which is difficult for the average person to understand. Why? They write prescriptions that nobody can read. Why? It's all done to preserve their mystique. They call the groin and the armpit the 'inguinal and axillary areas' so that you have to look the words up to know what they mean. It's all done so that you don't know what is happening.

There's a fear of people taking their own power and being responsible for themselves and their own lives. Society is threatened by that. Society is about rules. It's interesting that Germany, which has been at the root of the emergence of lots of these alternative therapies, has twice this century been a society that failed to take responsibility for itself. Where you have one extreme going on, you also find the other.

50

For Edward and me, the journey is just beginning. It's almost as if our marriage has just begun. We are only now just getting to know each other; we were living behind masks before.

My illness has been a turning point in my relationship with Edward as well as with myself. Suddenly I saw myself as a whole person and not just as an appendage to him. Me. Eileen. Not Eileen-and-Edward. For the first time ever I am in control of my life; no one else is pushing the buttons. If only someone had told me how easy it was! I felt in some ways very angry with myself that I had wasted all those years. But then death is such a motivator, and as Dr John says, we get the illnesses we need. Without that illness I wouldn't have had the motivation. I would have just gone on in the way I had done for the past forty years.

It was a terrible shock for Edward when I was diagnosed, but after I was able to take control it changed him. The illness opened up all kinds of things in our relationship. The biggest thing is that just as I started to have all kinds of insights, he did too, for himself. That first winter when his mother was ill was a tough time for him. Even though she had been overpowering in her love for him, they were close and he loved her very much. He got love and warmth from his mother, whereas his father dominated him. It's a time of huge stress, losing both your parents, and often grief has the effect of opening you up and making you vulnerable. What with both his parents dying and me being terminally ill, with three young children and the possibility of being on his own with them, Edward was under huge stress. I don't think I appreciated it because I was under total stress myself. I must have sucked him dry until I found out who I was. All the while he was holding down his job at the bank, and taking extended leave to go to California, where he was supporting the children and coming across the border to see me.

Early on I had said to Dr John, 'What if I suddenly find I don't want the life I've got?' When I told Edward that, he didn't say anything at all. He has always said to me, 'I think we are always going to be together.' His faith is stronger than mine. I feel that unless we move on together, the relationship is going to come apart. I said this to him and I think it frightened him. I felt very guilty because he has been so supportive, and this is a conflict for me. He has been incredible, and I couldn't have done it without him, so I feel as though I am sticking a knife in. But then it's a creative knife! I think that he is going to feel much better at the end. And it *is* the truth, what I am saying, because I am on a journey and I can't travel with somebody who is refusing to grow. It doesn't work, it really doesn't. Our pace of growth may be very different, and the way we grow may be very different. We can't necessarily go in parallel lines, but the fact is that we will both grow if Edward opens himself to it. That's the important thing, that there is mutual growth and movement, as opposed to stagnation for one partner and growth for the other.

All through our marriage before my illness I was dependent on him. I would never ever have said, 'Unless you are prepared to open your mind and grow with me, I don't want to be part of this relationship'. It's a big thing for him to deal with, and quite a shock for him.

Once life becomes comfortable again and the threat recedes, it's easy to slip back into your old ways. But I don't want to go back to living as we were before. I am a different person. I am helped in this by the diet – in a sense I *can't* ever go back because my diet is a huge statement about who I am and how I live, what I am doing to my body and the connections that I have made.

Edward has steadfastly refused to change his diet in any way. Although he was totally supportive of me, he stuck where he was regarding his eating habits. He is overweight and would admit to that. To a certain extent food has been a comfort for him through this time. It's been the thing that has kept him going. For instance, if the children had a bar of chocolate, he would say, 'Oh, please let me have a piece!', but then, just recently, he actually said, 'I want to shed this weight that I have put on, and I am only going to eat meat at the weekend,' which for him is a big step.

Helen is vegetarian anyway, but the boys are not and I don't believe in forcing it on them. You can't make somebody's journey for them; they have to do it themselves. It would have the opposite effect anyway – they'd run off to McDonald's behind my back. They have seen what has happened to me, and they have understood it. Despite the jokes about me and my diet, they are quite proud of what I've done.

51

Once I had had the hypnotherapy and released all those feelings, things changed. Edward had been married for fourteen years to this negative person who was unable to take any responsibility. All decisions were made by him and I was totally reliant on him. Suddenly here was this person who was the opposite. Edward could have hated that. But in fact he said that he welcomed it, and he loved it. It was what he had always hoped I would be, and suddenly I was! That's why Professor Stellart's remark about 'is your husband here?' incensed me so much: it would not have done a few months earlier. On all those early visits to St Lucy's, Edward came with me, then suddenly I said, 'I don't want you to come, I don't need you', and he felt fine about that, whereas before I would have been saying, 'Do you think we should . . . ?' Edward had always known this was there in me and had been waiting for it to come out.

The children were transformed, too. From walking around frightened on tiptoe they suddenly became normal children again when I was able to tell them what I had got. They found it frightening to start with because their idea of cancer was that you get it and you die. But once I had had the hypnotherapy, and all these feelings had come to the surface, and I was able to take control again, I told them, 'I've got lymphoma.' They said, 'What is that?' and I said, 'I've got all these tumours growing in my lymphatic system'. Even at the beginning I avoided using the word cancer. Then I did say it, and their faces were stricken. Now I know how people with Aids feel. Cancer was a word that they knew, and they immediately associated with dying. That was their first reaction: 'Are you going to die?'

At the beginning I would reply, 'Well, I hope not', because I wasn't strong enough in myself to say, 'No, I'm not'. But as time went on, until that awful time when I started going downhill again, I would say, 'No, I'm not going to'. The difference it made to them was huge. Once I became confident, the whole family situation changed. Instead of everyone being on edge and nervous with each other, we became closer than we had ever been.

I did in fact tell my oldest son about my abuse, and he was quite taken aback. The reason I told him was because he was the eldest and closest to me. I feel guilty that I didn't tell the other two. Perhaps I should – it's only when you can be totally honest and open about these things that they lose their power. It's only when you can't talk about them that they are powerful, that they have some sort of control over you. If people can see from this book that by being open and honest they will feel so much better, and can achieve what I have achieved, then perhaps it might help.

I had never thought of Edward as being a man to have insights. I realize now that there were a lot of deep parts of him which he never showed. In lots of ways I felt he was superficial. Everyone used to say that you never saw Edward down or in a bad mood. He was always on an even keel, always jokey – in fact, his jokiness used to irritate me. He would say that I took things so seriously. That aspect of me would irritate him, and he would make jokes and that would irritate me! And yet there were times when I knew that there was a lot more to him than he showed, more depth to him than he was prepared to show. But in all the years that we have been married, I never saw it very much, nor had he seen my positive side. The balance was adjusting, the scales levelling.

The new me was still consumed with dealing with my very sick body, but it had to be. I had to be focused. Nevertheless, he never queried anything I did. He supported me unequivocally.

It must have been a terrific learning curve for Edward too, on top of seeing all these horrible disgusting things happening to his wife. For the six months that I reeked of ammonia he used to get into bed and say, 'My God, this is horrendous'. He used to make my juices at the weekends and when I had to take my six o'clock enema he'd go down and fill the bucket with coffee. Once or twice when he was half asleep it was too hot ! And of course he cared for the children, taking them out and keeping life going for them as well.

He helped to find someone to come in three mornings a week, and then in the evening he would come home and often cook dinner for the children and do a juice for me. Some weekends I would stay in bed and he would look after me. It was obviously very stressful for him, but he kept me going through those times. If he hadn't, I couldn't have coped. He could have been one of those people who said, 'this is a waste of time; you're wasting money; it's cranky and it's not going to work' – but he didn't. He really supported me. Even when I went through that bad time in February 1994, I don't think he could really believe that it was all going to end. We'd come this far and he felt it couldn't fail now. He helped me to pull through.

52

Edward has been supportive emotionally, financially and practically. My children have been very supportive too – not so much practically as emotionally. It even got to the stage where we would all joke and they would say, 'How's your cancer today Mum?' It became almost as flippant as that. At the beginning of the therapy, when I was detoxifying, I got the most horrendous gas coming out of every orifice and the children would say, 'Oh, God! Environmental pollution, Mum!' and I would say, 'It's better out than in!' It was good to joke about it, because when they were full of fear they were too frightened to say anything. Before, they were compelled to wear a mask, and they couldn't show how they were feeling. After that things became more open and we could even laugh about it. Alex, the eldest, even said, 'If I ever get cancer I will know what to do.' To be able to make statements like that! To be open is very good for them. It stemmed purely from the fact that once my positive energy started to flow, they were enveloped in it. But before, with all this negativity coming from me, they were full of fear and bewilderment as to what was going on.

For Edward it could have been quite a threat; not only was I taking control and responsibility, but because I was opening up Pandora's box and letting all the horrid things float out, he not only had to be there observing, but he had to do it for himself too. That's not always comfortable! I saw another side of him that I hadn't seen before, and I was amazed at that. I was an avid reader of self-help books at this time and when I talked to him about them he would never say that he thought it was ridiculous. He listened, and he agreed with me. Having seen the transformation in me, he recognized the power, saw that it was real, that it wasn't just a straw to cling on to. That kept him going, because he knew that if he could keep my mind strong, then that would pull me through.

Perhaps I got the illness that Edward needed too for *his* opening. I was the leader in this area but he was ready for it, which was fantastic.

Edward loves science fiction. He sees what I am doing as related to sci-fi: outer space as a reflection of inner space. He sees it in terms of a journey, a journey into the unknown, just like a journey into space. Science fiction is the mythology of our time: *Star Wars*, *Star Trek*, *ET* – these very popular stories of our time helped him to see that you can get in touch with the mythological elements which are symbolic of something beyond. For Edward that has been his way, albeit unconscious, of contacting his inner strength.

When I talk about 'energies' he can recognize that there is a huge amount of energy around us: 'Like in *Star Wars* with Darth Vader and the negative force,' he said when we were talking about energy one day. Luke Skywalker goes to the little wise man where he learns to get in touch with The Force and Edward said, 'It's like getting in touch with the positive force inside yourself'. That is the perfect simile: the fact was that Luke was able to do wonderful things when he did connect with The Force inside him. It's a wonderful metaphor and very accessible, whereas a lot of the language of the New Age or popular psychology is not so accessible. Edward gets quite excited about that – he tells me, 'There you are. I told you that science fiction is not just a load of rubbish!'

53

It's all about trusting your own process. It's bought me this far, here I am, and that is amazing when I think about it. Having been at death's door so many times, I've had to trust in it and it has pulled me through. Often when people are ill, they turn to God and start praying. But if only they could see that the answer does not lie out there, but *in here*. It's not to say that it is not God; it's just that they are looking in the wrong place.

I had my ultimate test in 1993–4: 'My God, my God, why hast thou forsaken me?' The ultimate crisis before a resurrection. It's about keeping your faith, in yourself, in your own ability to overcome. I had to learn to listen to my own inner voice, to my instinct. When I last saw Dr John, he said to me, 'Just remember, always trust your instincts, because that is the true voice; that's the one that's telling you the truth, not these other voices. That can be very difficult. If you are really, really frightened, you don't hear those voices, you don't know what your instincts are. You lose your centre, you are all over the place.'

It's not easy to quantify the success of the Gerson therapy, because its success is very much up to you. It's not like orthodox medicine when you have things done *to* you, when you hand over your body to somebody else. With the Gerson therapy, it has got to be *you*, your will-power and spirit that does it. So if you are not in touch with that, then it is not going to work. That is the missing link. People ask me why it doesn't work with more people. Well, I think that the inner cleansing is the missing link, the psychological cleaning out.

I am excited by thinking that perhaps somebody reading this will make some connections. Telling the story has been therapeutic for me, and I have seen some things that I hadn't seen before. This book doesn't have to be just about cancer – because of the psycho-immunological aspect, we could be talking about any illness. I know that the Gerson therapy did help to save my life, but it wasn't the whole thing by any means. That's what makes this book different. The really important thing is the focus on the psychological side, and what light that throws on immunology.

54

I don't know where this journey is taking me. Before my illness I was a great one for living in the future: it was always what I was *going* to do. One of the things I have learned from being ill is that the past and the future are unimportant. The here and now is the only thing that matters. What's gone is gone and what is to come doesn't exist yet.

I feel very strongly – and this is the main reason for writing this book – that I would like to help people to see the whole picture of illness, and to understand that the emotional and other factors are just as important as the physical factors. We worry about what we are handed down genetically, in a physical sense, and not in a psychological sense. I look at my family and their patterns: they worry about the genetic time bomb that they have been handed in a physical sense, but I don't see it like that. I can defuse that bomb by taking out the psychological pin. Any one of us could have lived the perfect 'no stress, best diet' existence, but it wouldn't have made any difference if we ignored the psychological elements. Dr Winifred Rushforth, a psychologist who lived to nearly one hundred years old, when asked for her secret said, quick as a flash, 'I have always followed my unconscious!'. I thought, 'Yes! That's the answer. Follow your intuition and listen to your dreams.'

It was after the hypnotherapy that 'coincidences' started to arise. First of all, having suddenly been able to take control of my life, I went to that weekend retreat and I heard about the Gerson therapy for the first time. My in-laws both died, and suddenly there was the money. A friend came back into my life that I hadn't seen for some years, and lent us money, and provided somewhere for Edward and the children to stay. All these things just 'happened' to enable me to go down this path. It is almost as if every time I have been in some kind of crisis, something has appeared to help me. That in itself is very energizing.

I now see coincidences in a different way. I can't even accept the word any more – patterns, synchronicity, revelations are more appropriate. You decide on something, and once you're in tune with yourself, the answer appears. You become alive to these so-called coincidences, and it seems that nothing is by chance. Shakespeare said, *'There is a destiny that shapes our ends, rough hew it as we may.'* We may think we are rough-hewing our own path, but actually these things are being offered to us the whole time, and most of the time we don't see it. We call them coincidences, but they are actually our path.

55

My illness has certainly changed my perspective on my own life. Five years ago I viewed my childhood as happy. I didn't really want to look at my family and the way we were. That was the most painful part, having to admit that it wasn't perfect, having to demythologize it. And it wasn't perfect by a long way. I felt like a traitor, stepping outside the closeness of the family, even though the closeness was totally negative. In some ways I can see parallels with the path I took with the medical profession: you step outside and suddenly the closeness and the caring and the love disappears. That was my experience. While you stay in the family of orthodox medicine, you are treated in a certain way. It is the same in the family; you have got to play the game. So we are not talking about unconditional love and care here. This love is based on certain conditions: if you do these things, you will get this. As soon as you step outside, you are the outcast.

It has been shown, however, that eccentrics, the people who don't conform to the normal way of eating, of lifestyle and so on, actually live longer. Which implies that the rules of the game could damage your immune system! The rules *do* damage you; they damage the soul, and in a sense the soul is your immune system. It's your true path, and if you stray off the path, it's a harder job for your immune system. It puts a heavy burden on it.

Before my illness I had never looked on my life as a journey. I had always been in tune with nature, and I wasn't a total barbarian, but things that happened in my life I saw as fate. If anything, life was a journey over which I had no control whatsoever; it was ordained – a bit like the doctors saying, 'This is the progress of your disease and that's what's going to happen at the end of it'. That's how I saw my life. Until I had that amazing experience with Dr John, I didn't feel that I had any control over it. I saw events as random chance, and not as a gift to open up to. Everything was 'out there' rather than 'in here'. If things went wrong, it was someone else's fault; it wasn't mine. What I had done hadn't made it happen – I couldn't see the connection at all.

It made me understand that what is happening to me outside, is a reflection of what is happening to me inside. That's true for all of us because we all see the world in a different way, and we all have a different experience of the world. I made that connection, which was so energizing. It gives you enormous energy when you realize that all this power is inside yourself, and that it can influence everything you do. Obviously, things do happen over which we have no control, but the fact is that how we see them and what we do about them *is* within our control. Before, I was the personality type B, the helpless, hopeless cancer patient. If there was an enormous problem in my life, I would bury my head in the sand, and hope it would go away. I couldn't look it in the eye and confront it. I felt that I was powerless to deal with it. I hadn't contacted my own source of energy.

56

Meeting Dr John was another so-called 'coincidence'. The guides who are there to teach us something *do* come along in life – but we have to be open to them. They will never *not* be there, and that is where we have to take personal responsibility: we can walk straight past them if we choose. I am sure I had had many things thrust at me before I was ill, but it was only death that motivated me. If you aren't motivated by that, then nothing is going to motivate you.

As I saw my life, nothing had really gone right for me. I can see now that I was giving off negative energy and therefore I was getting negativity back. Now my life has changed for the better because I am full of much more positive energy. The energy you give out returns to you. I would hold my anger inside and all this negativity would be locked up. Friends and family used to ask me what was the matter, and I would say, 'NOTHING!' – my whole manner belying what I was saying. Like so many people, I was denying (even to myself) that I was angry.

The effect I started to have on other Gerson patients was that they received some of that positive energy, which before I just didn't have. Yvonne could see it, but she couldn't receive it. When you see that the flow of energy is free and eternal, you can give as much as you like; and the more you give, the more you have. When you absorb negative energy, you can feel the effect that it has on you, so one has to be skilful about what one is absorbing and what one is giving. It is a different way of looking at people and at life.

I used to control people with my negative energy all the time. I was a great one for using silence as a controller. I wouldn't lose my temper; I just wouldn't speak. People found it more infuri-ating than rage or expletives. Other people think you are not feeling, but in fact there's this turmoil going on inside, causing havoc. People were amazed to discover that this image of control was only a front.

But once I was diagnosed, the walls of Jericho fell down. The mask crumbled. We put on the mask which is the reverse of what is really going on, and we hide behind it. I told one friend that I felt I hadn't coped very well when the children were small and they said, 'But we looked on you as The One Who Coped!' I was amazed that they saw me like that. I had assumed that they could see through the façade. But I had obviously become very good at it. Look at all the energy that is used to hold this mask in place and stop it from cracking. Think of the drain on the immune system while you are doing this! I was projecting this negative energy all the time. It surprises me in a way that I got through my life as well as I did, considering the amount of negative energy I had inside me. But then I wasn't really doing all that well, because it was destroying me from the inside.

I have deliberately disengaged myself from some people, because whereas before they were giving me something, now they make me feel negative. I used to complain to people and they would complain back, but now I don't want to be near that sort of energy. I am learning to protect myself from other people's controlling energies. It is fortunate that Edward is the sort of person he is – he had to absorb a lot of my negative energy. He wore the opposite mask to mine – he saw life through rose-coloured spectacles and in some ways had a flippant approach. He now needs to look at *why* he needs to hide behind this clown mask. Life is a balance between being serious and being light-hearted. You need to be able to touch that serious side of yourself and not deny it. So the clown came in handy for a few years, but now perhaps he needs a rest.

The way I see it, we are living life against the rules of nature. An illness such as cancer is a signal to us: there is cause and effect, things go full circle, and if you behave in a certain way it rebounds on you. When people say to me, 'Why can't God save me or why doesn't he answer my prayers?', I say that he does; he *is* telling you something, but whether you choose to listen to the message or not is up to you. It is the voice within us; but people think of it as something 'out there'. They are not listening to the message from inside. It is so simple when you see it in those terms.

57

The most important thing for me in my recovery was clearing my past, going back and clearing out all the old stuff. That's an ongoing process – I'm not sure whether we ever finish; housework is never done! I mean that without taking anything away from the Gerson therapy – I know I wouldn't have survived without it. The key was taking responsibility for myself, and contacting that inner strength. I would never have *done* the Gerson therapy because I would have still been that helpless, hopeless person who would have said, 'I always knew something bad was going to happen to me' – a bit like Yvonne. I would have carried on playing the game by those rules and gone down a totally different path, but I was obviously ready to hear the message.

I feel now that part of my role is to pass the message on to other people, and to continue my own personal evolution, my own development, taking all these amazing things that have happened to me forward into life, and shedding the past.

There is a danger of getting too caught up in the past, instead of being in the here and now. There's a story about a Zen master and his student who were travelling along a road in China. They met a woman who was very rude and nasty to the Master and he replied quietly with a riddle. Some hours later they stopped to take some refreshment and the student said to him, 'Why did you reply so gently with that riddle?' The Master said to him, 'Why are you still back in that place? It's no longer in my consciousness!'

Dr John advised me, 'When you release these things, don't get drawn down the path of psychotherapy, of finding out *why* you did this and *why* you did that. It's come up, so learn from it, just put it where it belongs and let it go. Like the image of the river in Taoism, the river flows for ever and ever and all the water is miles down-river. What is the water doing here and now? We focus too much on the past – you often hear people say "Oh, she made me so angry" about something that happened three weeks ago and they are still carrying all this stuff around inside them.'

If you are living in the past, and thinking about the future, when are you ever actually *alive*? The past isn't alive, and the future isn't real – so when are *you* real? That is exactly how I was – I was living in a twilight world because I was never in the here and now. I was constantly thinking that tomorrow would be better. But when tomorrow came, it was just as bad and I started thinking about 'tomorrow' again. I was just existing, bombarded by the material world which gave me no space to explore this other experience. That attitude is detrimental to the spirit, as it doesn't feed the soul.

Before, all I could see was death; there was nothing at the end of the tunnel except death. It was like a huge blanket covering me and I was sending messages to every single cell in my body – I'm going to die. That's what happens to people who are newly diagnosed – this terrible focus on death. Because society doesn't want to talk about death, because we are all afraid of it, we can't help each other. Now, for me, there is nothing at the end of the tunnel except life. Death doesn't even enter into it now; it's gone.

Sometimes I wonder if I have really confronted dying. All I know is that it was terrifying for me before, but now I don't even think it is going to happen to me. Logically I know it's going to happen one day, but it goes back to living in the here and now; it's not something I need to think about. It's something that I will deal with on that day when it presents itself.

Death has a different meaning for me now. I see it as my soul going back into the vast unconsciousness and becoming part of a huge mass of energy again. That was not true before. It would have been obliteration and darkness. I see my body as a house for my soul, but it is nothing more than that. It is just dense matter. This ties in with the Gerson therapy which involves clearing out the physical body, the temple. If the body is the house and it has got a bit filthy and you clean it up, then it is a better place for the soul to live in – a simple concept. What we put in in terms of our food is either cleansing or not so cleansing. But the body is nothing once my soul has gone. I am happy for mine to be put on the tip. It's not something I shall need any more; I can just discard it like an old skin, so what does it matter what happens to it?

When my father died, I was the only one who refused to go and look at him. Some of the family were upset that I wouldn't go and said that he looked very peaceful. I said, 'It's not that. There's nothing there; it's just a body.' When my brother Harry died a few years ago, my sister-in-law asked if I was going to come to the

Chapel of Rest. I said no and she said, 'Would you rather remember him as he was?' and I said, 'Yes, but the fact is that it was just a body; it's nothingness.'

The way I see death now is that we all live on in that great mass out there. The fear of death is more bound up with the personality than the soul. Grief of losing one of my children would be the loss of having that personality there day to day, yet my grief would not be for the soul; I would be happy for the soul.

58

Man is going off into space thinking that it will give us all the answers. Talk about being out there instead of in here! If we look to our own inner journey, we will find the answers there. Outer space and science fiction, our current mythologies, lead us to think in terms of 'out there' and not actually see what the reflection is 'in here'. It's one simple connection to make. It is exciting when you begin to look at what the mirror is holding up to you.

We have all got to go down into that pit before we learn. Edward could see that when we talked about it. There are two sorts of people who have these insights: the wise and the sick. The wise get the insights *before* they get ill! But most of us have got to look down into the abyss before we say, 'Yes, I'm prepared to change'.

You have to go through a personal hell in order to open these doors because it requires tremendous force to open them. Edward went through his personal hell when I was ill. It ties up with the Christian symbology of death and resurrection: you can look at it as a form of personal resurrection. I almost literally came back from the dead. For me, it was a rebirth.

It was like a reset button, a chance to start again, which negates the pessimistic saying that life isn't a rehearsal! There *is* a chance to replay if you wake up in time. I did feel angry that it took me nearly fifty years to wake up, but then mid-life is our time to wake up – we are not equipped with the experience or maturity or whatever else it requires in our twenties or thirties. It's when we are *meant* to wake up, and that's why mid-life crisis is part of our language. Most people are given a crisis of some kind and it's a question of what they do with it. You can sit and be miserable for the rest of your life, or you can pick up your cudgels and deal with the situation.

There I was teetering over the edge, and I have clawed my way back. Sometimes I think, 'Well! What do I do now? What next?' I feel a bit like the hero in the film who fights his way through the crocodiles and then stands victorious as the film ends. The End. Moment of triumph. But what next? We never know the rest of the story!

It's part of being human that at the beginning I felt how wonderful and precious life was, but it is very easy to slide back and take things for granted. Sometimes I have to kick myself and remember how it felt. But I can't live on that intense edge all the time. I just need to access it from time to time, and not walk past the miracle of my existence, the miracle of spring every year. The trouble is that we are often overwhelmed by the terrible things that happen in the world, and we are blind to Nature, who is showing us her wonderful things which we hardly notice.

People who step outside and do what makes them happy and not what society thinks they should do are regarded as eccentric. But they are courageous; they are taking a risk by trusting their inner voice. Even when things were very bad, I never believed that I was going to die. Before I met Dr John, death overwhelmed me; every thought was death and that was the big difference between how I was then and how I am now.

Suddenly I have got my life back, and it frightens the hell out of me. I now have actually got to deal with life! It's very invigorating and exciting, but there is a scary element to it too. There is a huge sense of anti-climax after the great drama of the illness, but I think the best is yet to come. It took courage to step out of the circle, but now, for me, it definitely takes more courage to live than to die. Before, Death was my consciousness; now, Life is. That's the difference.

Further Reading

BOOKS

Bass, Eileen, and Davies, Laura, *The Courage to Heal*, Cedar, New York, 1988

Bishop, Beata, *A Time to Heal*, Penguin, Harmondsworth, UK, 1985

Bond, Jean, *Behind the Masks*, Gateway, Bath, UK, 1993

Chopra, Deepak, *Quantum Healing: exploring the frontiers of mind/body medicine*, Bantam, London, UK, 1989

Dethlefsen, Thorwald, and Dalke, Rudiger, *The Healing Power of Illness*, Element, Shaftesbury, UK, 1997

Gerson, Dr Max, *A Cancer Therapy*, Gerson Institute/Station Hill Press (PULSE), California, USA, 1958

Levenson, Frederick, *Causes and Prevention of Cancer*,

Levine, Stephen, *Guided Meditation, Exploration and Healings*, Gateway, Bath, UK, 1991

Martin, Paul, *The Sickening Mind*, HarperCollins, London, UK, 1997

May, Robert, *Physicians of the Soul*, Element, Shaftesbury, UK, 1991

Miller, Alice, *Banished Knowledge*, Virago, London, UK, 1990

—*Breaking Down the Wall of Silence*, Virago, London, UK, 1991

—*Drama of the Gifted Child*, Virago, London, UK, 1987

—*The Untouched Key*, Virago, London, UK, 1990

—*Thou Shalt Not Be Aware*, Virago, London, UK, 1984

Morris, Nat, *The Cancer Blackout*, Regent House, USA, 1959

Rushforth, Dr Winifred, *Ten Decades of Happenings*, Gateway, Bath, UK, 1984

le Shan, Lawrence, *You Can Fight for Your Life, Emotional factors in cancer*, M Evans and Co, USA

Siegel, Bertie, *Living, Loving and Healing*, Aquarian, London, UK, 1993

St Aubyn, Lorna, *Today is a Good Day to Die*, Gateway, Bath, UK, 1991

Strettbacher, J Konrad, *Making Sense of Suffering*, Dutton, New York, USA, 1993

PAPERS

Eysenck, Hans 'Health's character', in *Psychology Today*, December 1988

Gar, Hildenbrand, *et al* 'Five year survival rates of melanoma patients', Alternative Therapies in Health and Medicine, September 1995, Vol 1, no 4

Martin, Paul, 'Psychology and the immune system', in *New Scientist*, 8 April 1987

Reed, James and Sikora, 'British oncologists evaluate Gerson cancer treatment', in *The Lancet*, 336(8716), 18 September 1990

'The story of Ian Gawler', *Australian Medical Journal* 1978, 2, 433

Useful Addresses

Cancer Control Society
2043 N.Berendo Street
Los Angeles
CA 90027
Tel: 213 663 7801
Advises on non-toxic cancer therapies and nutrition

The Gawler Foundation
Yarra Valley Living Centre
PO Box 77G
Yarra Junction
Victoria 3979
Australia
Tel: 0061 5 967 1730

The Gerson Institute
PO Box 430
Bonita
California 92002
Tel: 619 585 7600
Fax: 619 585 7610

International Foundation of Practitioners of Natural Therapeutics
10 Copse Close
Sheet
Petersfield
Hants GU31 4DL
United Kingdom
Tel: (0)1730 266790
Fax: (0)1730 260058

World Cancer Research Fund
105 Park Street
London W1Y 3FB
United Kingdom
Tel: (0)171 343 4200
An international report on the links between diet and cancer

UK

Gerson Support Group
c/o Lesley Pearce
1 Park Rise Close
Leatherhead
Surrey
KT22 7JA
Tel: (0)1372 817652
Fax: (0)1372 386049
URL: www.webserve.co.uk/gerson

British Council of Hypnotist Examiners
Head Office
Blinking Sike
Caxton Way
Eastfield Business Park
Scarborough YO11 3YT
Tel: (0)1723 585960

General Council and Register of Consultant Herbalists
PO Box 10388
London N16 9BQ
Tel: (0)171 503 7980

Bristol Cancer Help Centre
Grove House
Cornwallis Grove
Clifton
Bristol
BS8 4PG
Tel: (0)117 9743216
Helpline: (0)117 9809505

The Hale Clinic
7, Park Crescent
London W1N 3HE
Tel: (0)171 631 0156/637 3377

Organic Suppliers

Barleycorn
97–99 Lancaster Road
Enfield
Middlesex
Tel (for delivery): (0)181 363 2345

Choice Organics
Unit 2
Atlas Transport Estate
Bridges Court off York Road
London SW11 3QS
Tel: 0171 924 1700/1744
The largest distributor of organic produce in the UK. Widespread delivery.

Planet Organic
42 Westbourne Grove
London W2 5SH
Tel: (0)171 221 7171

The Soil Association
86 Colston Street
Bristol BSI 5BB
Tel: (0)117 929 0661
Can provide details of organic suppliers.

Wild Oats
210 Westbourne Grove
London W11 2RH
Tel: (0)171 229 1063

Wholefoods
24 Paddington Street
London W1M 4DR
Tel: (0)171 935 3924

Most major supermarkets have a small selection of organic fruit and vegetables.